The Inscrutable
Dr. Hare

The Inscrutable Dr. Hare

Bob Robertson

H&H PUBLICATIONS   Oro Valley, Arizona

Copyright © 1996 by Bob Robertson

This special edition was prepared for printing by
Ghost River Images
1600 East Roger Road #22
Tucson, Arizona 85719.

Printed in the United States of America

First Printing: 1997

10 9 8 7 6 5 4 3 2 1

ISBN 0-9656321-0-5: $19.95
ISBN 0-9656321-1-3 (pbk): $12.95

H&H PUBLICATIONS
12995 North Oracle Road, #141, Box 204
Oro Valley, AZ 85737

Contents

For Hazel

ACKNOWLEDGMENTS

Only with the blessing, patience and understanding of Hazel Shaw Hare was this story possible. She shared her recollections and made her address book available for contacts with former associates and relatives.

Without Harry N. Jacobs, former engineer with Airborne Instruments Laboratory, and, importantly, with the American Broadcasting Company, there would not have been a substantial chapter to this story. And quite possibly there might not have been such a successful Grass Valley Group.

Ruth Kuntz Towne, Dr. Hare's loyal assistant, recalled the difficult days and the good times.

Bill and Pat Rorden shared their recollections and box of newspaper clippings Pat had collected.

Bob Johnson recalled some of his experiences as the longest serving employee of the Grass Valley Group.

Obie Langford, recently retired, told of the activities of Dr. Hare as Director of Research at Texaco, furnished copies of all the patents and a copy of the report of the activities of the Airborne Instrument Laboratory during World War II.

Roy Mazzagatti, retired engineer of Texaco, related his experiences with Dr. Hare.

John D. Hare II furnished genealogical information and insight about the Hare family.

George H. Hare for sharing the research of Dr. Moore.

Dr. Ronald M. Moore contributed a wealth of information about the lives of Drs. George and Jessie Hare, Dr. Donald Hare's parents.

R. A. Isberg reported his experiences at Airborne Instruments Laboratory and shared documents.

Rebecca Greer, Fresno, California, a professional researcher, ferreted out many details of the lives of the Hare family.

James Lycett, former editor and feature writer of the Detroit News, for his patience, valuable editorial advice and encouragement.

Mary Ann Robertson (no relation) with her computer opened the library at Stanford.

Roger Milliken, Chairman and Chief Executive Officer of Milliken & Company.

My wife and reader, Esther, for her understanding of my preoccupation with this undertaking.

PREFACE

On a Saturday morning early in June I went to the plant and it changed my life, perhaps saved it. The offices were quiet, not many executives were around. Those who came in were dressed very casual, sport shirts or "yard clothes" in contrast to jacket and tie during the week. As I walked past the office of Charles Lanphier, president of the Sangamo Electric Company in Springfield, Illinois, he looked up from his work and nodded. I acknowledged the gesture with, "Good morning, Chick," went on with my errand and returned to my office.

The telephone was ringing. It was Cecil Clark, a company vice president, "Chick just called me and asked if you had a job yet. I said I didn't think so. You haven't, have you?"

"Nothing definite," I replied.

"Come on over. Chick made a suggestion. I think we should talk about it."

I didn't know what to expect. Six months before I had told Clark I wanted to leave the area to try a different climate. A series of specialists had tried and failed to control my asthma attacks which were coming more frequently and impaired my ability to function. There was no guarantee a change of climate would help, but we had tried everything else. Some of my responsibilities included handling confidential information which had to be carefully transferred to other employees, hence the reason for the six months notice. In exchange for the long notice I was given the privilege of taking whatever time off I needed for interviews with potential employers in the west.

Time was running out. I might be heading west unemployed.

As I entered Clark's office he said, "Close the door."

"Do you know Dr. Hare?"

"Not really. I remember seeing him around a few times. Heard he quit after Sangamo bought his company."

"Chick says Dr. Hare's got some new products in the TV industry and the company is going great guns. They patched up their differences after he quit and Chick's even on his board of directors. He said Dr. Hare needs someone like you."

Clark paused for a minute like he was reconsidering whether to say what he was thinking.

He continued, "Dr. Hare is a helluva hard guy to get along with, I know from experience, and I imagine tough to work for. Frankly, I would think twice before sending a well guy out there, let alone someone with a health problem. Chick said if you're interested he'll call Dr. Hare and set up an interview. What do you think?"

"I'd like to give it a shot. Tell Chick yes."

"You gonna be around for a while this morning?"

"A couple of hours."

"Chick may try to call him right away. I'll let you know."

I returned to my office. Thirty minutes later Clark called.

"Chick said Dr. Hare wants to talk to you. Next Thursday. The old bastard said he would pay half your air fare and if you take the job he'll pay the other half. That's just like him."

I flew to Sacramento, rented a car, drove up to Grass Valley and out a few miles in the country to Dr. Hare's company, the Grass Valley Group. Driving up the driveway past the plant entrance I noticed there was only one car parked in front of the building, the rest in back. Assuming the car in front was for someone special, like Dr. Hare. I parked in back, not wanting to get off to a bad start.

When I walked in Dr. Hare was sitting at his table, casually dressed in a short-sleeved sport shirt and khaki trousers; quite a contrast to the white shirt, tie and jacket corporate atmosphere I was used to. After the introductory handshakes he dominated the conversation telling me about the company and its rapid growth. He showed me through the plant, one 4,000 square foot building, which didn't take long. When we returned to his office he got to the purpose of my visit.

"If you take the job you'll start as the Controller. That will be your main responsibility. We're a small company and we all do many things. You will be given more duties as time goes on." He looked at his watch. "Right now we go to lunch. I want you to meet Hazel."

Dr. Hare led the way out the front door to that one car. I started to get in on the passenger side, but he pushed me aside and got in with a puzzled look on his face. So he wants me to drive, I thought. I went around and got in the driver's seat. There was no key in the ignition.

"Give me the keys," I said as I held out my hand.

"Keys, hell, I don't have the keys. I thought this was your car."

"And I thought it was yours. Mine is in the back parking lot." So much for first impressions.

We walked around back, got in my rented car and drove up to his house, high on the company property. I met Hazel Hare, we had a nice lunch and talked no business. The conversation was about the walnut dining table made by an Italian craftsman, the problems they had with the contractor who built the house and the design of the free-standing fireplace. Before we returned to the plant he had a private conversation with Hazel. I was sure Dr. Hare was getting her impression of me.

When we sat down in his office I opened the conversation, "It looks like you have a job that needs filled and I would like to have it. You know about my asthma problem?"

"Yes. Chick told me. We'll get that fixed," he said with confidence. "My brother was a medical doctor. He introduced me to my internist who was the Chief of Staff of the University of California Hospital. He'll know who's the best in that field."

He resumed, "We haven't talked about salary."

"I'm not concerned. You'll pay me what I'm worth to you."

"I know your present salary at Sangamo."

"That doesn't surprise me."

Dr. Hare hadn't ask me a single question about my qualifications or what my job was at Sangamo. Apparently Chick Lanphier had told him all he wanted to know, including my salary.

"I'll start you at $100 a month less than you're making now."

"When do I start?"

"As soon as you can get here. Hazel will try to find you a house to rent. That's no easy job in this little community, but she knows how."

Hazel found and rented a house for us. Six weeks after we moved in I got a retroactive raise in pay. Dr. Hare said, "I just wanted to see how much you wanted to come here. You know one thing that impressed me? You didn't ask me about what kind of medical insurance plan we had, or vacation policy, or retirement."

This was the man I came to admire and with whom I became a close friend for many years. His life is a story that needed to be told and I nominated myself to tell it. He did not make the task easy. While not secretive about his past, he often related incidents of his earlier years, but he left few tracks. Fortunately many of his associates were willing to describe their experiences. He was the first to admit he was opinionated and difficult to work for, but many had their lives profoundly influenced by his tenets.

His was not an easy life despite his extraordinary intelligence. In one of his pensive moods he said, "I was born with this gift. I didn't do anything to deserve it. But with it came a drive and sense of responsibility to use it,

v

sometimes at the price of happiness. It's the same with Chick, he's had a lot of unhappiness in his life."

This is a story of real people, real incidents and wherever possible, real names. Most conversations and scenes are vivid recollections, a few are reconstructed from factual situations.

From the time he completed his Ph.D. this extraordinary man was referred to, almost without exception, as "Dr. Hare." He did not use the title of doctor when he introduced himself or answered the telephone, and he never asked that his associates call him Dr. Hare. Perhaps it was his carriage, his scholarly look, or an aura that radiated a compelling use of the title, a show of respect. In the office Hazel Hare always referred to him as Dr. Hare. Bill Rorden worked closely with him for 14 years and remained a close friend for another 11 years and never called him "Donald." The same with me. On the golf course Bob Johnson may have called him an unflattering name in jest, but he never called him "Donald." All would have been uncomfortable using his first name. In the business, son Stephen always addressed or referred to him as Dr. Hare, never as "Dad."

Chick Lanphier was an exception, he liked first names. He was quick to tell an associate who addressed him as Mr. Lanphier, "Call me Chick." He called Dr. Hare "Donald" except when he referred to him, then he always used "Dr. Hare."

B. R.

1962
GRASS VALLEY, CALIFORNIA

Saturday morning Dr. D. G. C. Hare donned his gray canvas pork-pie golf hat with a maroon band and left his A-frame house, high up on the company property, to drive down to the plant. The two Dachshunds who usually went with him were chasing a lizard. As he opened the door to the small, five-year-old black Mercedes they stopped their game, stood still side by side on the deck under the railing, looking out at him. Only their tails wagged to get his attention. When the car door closed without a call from him they stared with disbelief.

He wanted to be alone.

The parking lot at the plant was vacant. He parked close to the building and got out of the car. A lizard streaked past him into the safety of the bushes. A pair of swallows swooped by from their mud nest high on the concrete block wall under the eaves above the rear door of the building. The surface of the tranquil lake was rippled by a pair of Mallards as they paddled into the dark blue patches of the reflection from the surrounding lawn and trees. An unnatural silence filled the building as he walked through the metal shop past the bottled water stand and the counter with the coffee pot. His sneakers made almost no noise on the asphalt tile. He stopped momentarily in front of shelves stocked with several models of finished audio amplifiers, all waiting for buyers. A slight glow from the test instruments that were never turned off emitted the only light in the room other than white shafts of early daylight from the numerous windows, but shaded most of the day by the wide overhanging roof.

In his office he settled his lean, six-foot-plus frame into his old, well-worn but friendly oak swivel chair. On the shelves above the table against the wall were copies of scientific publications he so carefully collected and had professionally bound each year.

Out of habit he reached for the ever present slide rule on the table. He stared at it as if he had never seen it before, then laid it back down. No, he didn't need any calculations to know that time could be running out for this company unless some new business showed up soon. He was not disconsolate, just worried. Looking out the big window he saw a colorful picture postcard, the mountain ash and weeping willow beside the lake with a backdrop of fir and ponderosa pines. God, how he loved this place.

Balancing on the edge of financial disaster was nothing new to him. Maybe it was in his genes. His parents led an affluent life until they lost everything in retirement and had to go back to work. He scrounged for every penny when he enrolled at Stanford, not knowing from one school quarter to the next if he could earn enough to stay in school.

Then for years he had the security of doing research for Texaco, followed by the war years engrossed in the development of defense measures. He remembered the day he quit the Deering-Milliken job to start his own firm, the D. G. C. Hare Company. A smile crossed his face with the recollection of the secretary at Stanford who typed his résumés and suggested he use all the initials of his names. "People won't remember Donald Hare like they will Donald G. C. Hare," she told him. Now he needed more than just remembrance, he needed business. The multi-channel tape recorders he developed were exciting and challenging and he felt he made the best. In fact, he knew they were the best. The Cinerama job took imagination to manufacture the multiple speaker sound amplification to match the advanced triple screen movie projection for specially built theaters. Then the M.I.T. contract and a study for the government on the use of solid state components, the newest development in electronics, helped pay the rent. He had a small, competent organization but found it difficult to keep the pipeline full. When things got tough he sold the Hare Company to Sangamo. Even though it bore his name, somehow he didn't feel as emotionally attached to it as he did to his latest endeavor, the Grass Valley Group.

Was there a pattern emerging? Was he destined to bring a company just so far and then have to let it go? This time it was more serious. Before it had been only his own money, with no other investors involved. As an employer he felt some obligation to his people to provide them jobs, but they had not invested money in the company. When the wolf sniffed at the door again a few months ago, Bill Rorden invested his life savings in the company. He would have it on his conscience if Bill were to lose it. Sure, they still had a consulting contract with Sangamo, but that alone wasn't enough. Even an increase in orders for the audio equipment wouldn't help much because of the low gross profit margin caused by intense competition. They needed a proprietary product. Bill was the brightest engineer he had ever worked with and could get a job anywhere in industry. But he wanted to keep him. Together they should be able to do great things. They can make anything. Anything! If only they could find the key. And he felt responsible for the key.

Lean years were no strangers to Dr. Hare, but 1962 had been a financial disaster. On the upside, he was 55, in good health, weighed the same as he did in high school. He rose out of his chair, picked up his walking stick, a battered old two-iron, and headed out onto the property. Stopping occasionally to look at a tree or a rock formation, he walked some 300 yards clear to the top of the sloping terrain, tapping the golf club on the ground. Behind the redwood water tank stood the leaning silver gray trunk of the widowmaker that had been there for many years before he bought the property; he stopped and wondered when it might come crashing down. Like his company it was still hanging on. The breeze stirring the leaves of the Manzanita bushes and needles of the trees made the only audible sound except for an occasional bark from his puppies on the deck of the house. "The 100-mile view" he called it as he looked out over the valley for a long time. This he did not want to lose, this cloistered space in the foothills of the Sierras.

He strolled down the hill to his car with perhaps more optimism than at the start of the day.

Building No. 1   The Grass Valley Group

5

A LEGACY

If heredity plays an important part in one's total makeup, Donald Hare's parents were significant other than just bringing him into this world.

George Andrew Hare was born at Mount Pleasant, Iowa, March 23, 1857, the son of Jacob and Mary Ann (Corkhill) Hare. In 1884 he graduated from Iowa Wesleyan College with a degree of Bachelor of Science. In college he had a part time job as a reporter for the Burlington Hawkeye. After college he spent two years in southern Florida where he taught school. He subsequently entered the University of Michigan at Ann Arbor, where he studied medicine and graduated with an M.D. degree in 1887.

While in medical school he married Jessie Blanche Daniells on December 23, 1886. She was born in West Union, Iowa, April 13, 1862, and was the daughter of Dr. Thomas and Mary Jane Daniells. Dr. Daniells was a physician originally practicing at Rutland, Vermont. Because of his wife's ill health they had decided to go west but got only as far as Iowa when she died of tuberculosis. It was there that George and Jessie first met.

Jessie went to Battle Creek, Michigan, at the age of 14 and eventually entered the school of nursing. She became Dr. John Harvey Kellogg's private office nurse at the Battle Creek Sanitarium and was instrumental in setting up the first diagnostic laboratory used by that hospital. She wanted to practice medicine like her father, but the University of Michigan, following the same policy of female discrimination found in most American medical schools at the time, rejected her application. But the the school finally changed its policy and she was accepted the first year women were allowed to enroll. She graduated in 1887, in the same class as her husband, and became one of the country's few female physicians.

Dr. George A. Hare did postgraduate work at Harvard in 1887, then returned to Iowa Wesleyan College to complete a Master of Science Degree in 1889. Dr. Jessie D. Hare took additional training in New York.

The Hares then moved to Battle Creek, where he worked as a staff physician at the Battle Creek Sanitarium for a short time. There they had their first son, Herald. They were well acquainted with the director, Dr. John Harvey Kellogg, and the Kellogg brothers Will and George who founded the Kellogg Food Company. Dr. Kellogg was impressed with the writings of a Mrs. Ellen White who was active in the Seventh-Day Adventist movement. She was considered a visionary, the discoverer of a "water cure" and vegetarianism and insisted on the six-day creation belief calling for the Saturday sabbath. Dr. Kellogg was the most prominent member of the church and exerted pressure for medical and education reform. His views possibly influenced the Hares to become devout followers of that religion. While at Battle Creek, Dr. Jessie Hare assisted in the development of a coffee-like beverage made from cereal for a patient, Charles Post, who liked it so much he later manufactured it in his own company, the Post Cereal Company, and called it Postum.

Less than a year later Dr. George Hare resigned from the staff at Battle Creek and became superintendent of the Mt. Vernon Sanitarium in Ohio from 1888 until 1891. There they had their second son, Gail. They moved to Fresno, California, to set up a general practice and a sanitarium. Dr. George Hare even during his early years had taken a special interest in the newly developing field of endocrinology and had a special concern for the treatment of tuberculosis which was so prevalent.

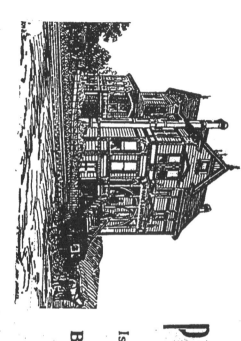

Dr. Hare's
PRIVATE SANITARIUM
Cor. K and Stanislaus

Is prepared to give First-class Sanitarium Treatment. ELECTRICITY and MASSAGE used scientifically.

Baths, Russian, Turkish, Electro Medicated, Etc.

TRAINED ATTENDANTS

Treatment with or without board. Rates very reasonable.

TELEPHONE RED 311

Advertisement in 1898 Fresno City Directory

10

They started Hare's Private Sanitarium in 1891, moved to a different location in 1892 and changed the name to Fresno Medical and Surgical Sanitarium. Two more children were born into the family, Helen in 1895 and Marion in 1897.

The Hares' move to Fresno probably was influenced by Moses J. Church, one of that city's early pioneers and the founder, in 1888, of the Fresno Sanitarium, the first such private facility in that area. Church, an early entrepreneur, was considered by many as the father of irrigation in the San Joaquin Valley. He was assisted in starting the sanitarium by Dr. Merritt G. Kellogg, a brother of Dr. John Harvey Kellogg and the other Kellogg brothers of Battle Creek.

The Hares' early facilities are said to have housed the first outpatient surgery in Fresno, and they were pioneers in x-ray in the west. Dr. George Hare was intrigued by anything new in medical science. When he learned of Wilhelm Roentgen's discovery of the x-ray in 1895 he had to have an x-ray machine. He tried to buy one in the east right after the turn of the century. Unable to purchase a machine, he set about to make his own. He wound his own electrical transformers and experimented until he had a working machine. An x-ray film, thought to be one of the early ones taken by him in 1903, is on display in one of the offices of the Fresno-Madera Medical Society. This x-ray was generated by a static plate machine that required a 30-minute exposure and includes much of the upper right part of the body. He continued to experiment and improve his machine and originally did all of the x-ray work for the

Burnett Sanitarium, which eventually became the Fresno Community Hospital.

In 1904-1906 the Hares went back east to Washington, D. C. and organized the Washington Sanitarium Association which became the Washington Adventist Hospital. It was located first in a home once owned by General Grant and later into Tacoma Park, Maryland. At that time Dr. George Hare also became the associate editor of the magazine, Life and Health, which is one of the oldest health journals in America. He was asked to join the election campaign of Theodore Roosevelt but turned it down because he wouldn't discuss financial matters on a Saturday.

Also in 1906 Dr. George Hare served as a delegate to the International Medical Congress in Lisbon, Portugal. The King of Portugal extended the Hares an invitation to dinner, but they declined because it was to be held on a Saturday. While in Europe Dr. George Hare took a postgraduate course at the University of Vienna. Dr. Jessie went along and took additional training in Germany in the field of gynecology, her special interest. Perhaps it was the romance of the travel, or the elegant surroundings, or the relaxed old world atmosphere, but somewhere between Lisbon and Germany, Jessie became pregnant. She was in her 45th year and her youngest daughter was nine years old. With her medical knowledge and specialty it is hard to believe this pregnancy was unplanned. Still, perhaps at that time she may have been considered past child bearing age. When they returned to California Donald George Corkhill Hare was delivered on May 31, 1907. He was given the second middle name, Corkhill, for his grandmother's maiden name. She came from the Isle of Man in the Irish Sea, 20 miles south of Scotland.

Dr. George Hare's chief recreation was the cultivation of flowers and fruit. He was well known as a grower of table grapes, and prior to 1915 had nearly 200 acres in cultivation. The distinction of "table grapes" was important since Jessie was an active member of the Women's Christian Temperance Union and would not have permitted the grapes to be sold to a winery. For several years between 1908-1913 Dr. George Hare's grapes were stated to have brought the highest prices on the Chicago market. A freight carload sold for as much as $2,900. However, there was no evidence his venture into the vineyard business was profitable as he apparently continuously had money problems. He was instrumental in founding the Fresno Fruit Growers Company, and served as that organization's vice-president.

Dr. George Hare's digressions from medical practice into agriculture and other entrepreneurial efforts consumed much of his time and frequently met with financial disaster. He had acquired several "ranches," one of which was next to a tree nursery owned by T. Kugiya. He bought 3,000 orange trees at five cents per tree from the nursery owner. They had a written agreement the trees could remain on Kugiya's property through the year 1907, but if they were still there in 1908 Hare agreed to pay rent of ten dollars for the use of the land. The two got into a hassle over access to the property. Hare accused Kugiya of not allowing his workers to tend to the trees and making threats of violence. In June, 1909, Dr. Hare went to court and got an injunction against Kugiya stating the trees were budding and needed attention or he would be damaged in the amount of $900. Ten days later the judge dismissed the injunction so Hare sued for damages of $500. Kugiya filed a cross suit and claimed he was damaged in the amount of $300. The court found the allegations of both parties were untrue, except that Kugiya had been damaged by the amount of $10 and awarded him that amount plus costs.

In 1911 Dr. George Hare subscribed for 5,000 shares of the capital stock of Sacramento Holding Company and gave two notes in payment. He never paid the notes and was taken to court.

Hare was a partner in another large real estate transaction that included almost two sections of land for $20,000, bought with $500 down and a series of five notes. It was subsequently foreclosed.

The doctor became involved with three other partners in the development of a mining property called the "Uncle Sam" mine. They were sued for wages not paid in the amount of $512.50 for 205 days work at $2.50 per day. Dr. Hare was in court often for not paying workers on his ranches.

Dr. Hare was a partner to one individual in several of the land ventures and perhaps was being used because of his good reputation in the medical community. He was named frequently in suits for unpaid wages for work on the properties and failure to pay notes when due.

Drs. Jessie and George Hare bought some raw land and also real estate lots which they were unable to pay for and lost on foreclosures.

The one time Dr. George Hare ended up in court because of his medical practice he went eight miles out into the country to the home of a patient, took her to Fresno and put her in care of a nurse. Her husband objected but Dr. Hare persisted and sent him a bill for her care. The husband refused to pay so Dr. Hare filed a suit against the husband for $382.50. Dr. Hare persuaded the woman to file for divorce, which she did. The husband paid for the nursing care before the divorce, but won the case against Dr. Hare for all subsequent treatments and was awarded damages and costs.

In 1913 The Hares moved their residence to a site of a double lot on which a separate building was built to house a three-car garage, workshop, laundry room downstairs and five rooms upstairs for the medical examining rooms, bathroom and x-ray room. Later these structures became listed in Fresno's Local Register of Historic Resources. It was at this location Donald spent most of his formative years.

His was not a typical childhood as he had no friends his own age. The two brothers and two sisters were much older and had their own interests and friends. Donald was not included. Doctors' offices were not an appropriate playground so most of the time he was around adults. In his after-school hours he had to fend for himself. He wandered in and out of the small medical complex and saw people with problems, some in pain, waiting to see his father or mother. Although Donald had no thought of becoming a medical doctor (he didn't have the stomach for it), the medical books in his father's office attracted him. One day he discovered Gray's Anatomy. At every opportunity he smuggled it to his room where hours were spent reading and studying the illustrations. From it he learned Latin, and about sex.

Mealtime for the Hares was seldom a family gathering. There was no reliable time for them to expect to have dinner. Donald's father or mother could be detained by a patient, his older siblings were busy with their own activities, and his father often dined out at civic or medical meetings. Donald never experienced a solid family relationship. Occasionally an older brother would play cards or chess with him, but there were few activities that involved the whole family.

Although the doctor was very outgoing to adults, he and Donald were not close. Dr. George Hare liked to be the center of attention in organizations and devoted much of his time with them at the neglect of his practice and family. But his ego had to be pampered. He was a dapper dresser and fast and loose with his money, some of which had been borrowed from relatives.

Dr. George Hare had a strong interest in the scientific training of medical students and was active in the American Academy of Medicine, which was organized to improve the standard of medical education in America. The National Academy elected him president in 1916-1917. This organization was successful in closing at least 75 of the more inefficient medical schools, which represented about half of the total number of medical schools in America at that time. In addition to serving as president of the Fresno County Medical Society in 1899 and 1904, he was a district councilor for the California State Medical Society for five years, and was twice elected as vice president of the California Medical Society. He served as a member of the House of Delegates of the American Medical Association from 1912-1915.

As a prominent citizen in Fresno, he belonged to the California Historical Society, the Commercial Club, the University Sequoia Club, the Beta Theta Pi Fraternity and the Seventh-Day Adventist Church. Young Donald saw little of him as he was always leaving to attend a meeting. This was an affluent family into which, from all outward appearances, Donald was fortunate to have been born. But Dr. George Hare's adventures in real estate speculation constantly depleted the family finances.

The Hare's contributed to the church regularly, saw to it that the children were baptized and attended the church school. George and Jessie were devout in their religious beliefs and so young Donald was enrolled in the church school. Donald's intellect and personality created problems they had never experienced with the other four children.

In the early days of grade school he was a distraction, sent home to be disciplined by his father, and suspended. After a scolding from his parents, and an additional contribution to the church by his father, Donald was reinstated. Several times. Neither his parents nor teachers realized the problem was boredom with the simple tasks in school and that Donald had a gift of exceptional intelligence. His knowledge was well beyond his years for a normal child. At the age of seven he completely disassembled a clock and put it back together. He built a short wave radio and was intrigued with guns and explosives. Once he put a bullet on a stone and struck it with a hammer. The explosion sent the lead bullet one way and the brass casing the other. Lucklly, Donald was not injured but unfortunately the bullet put a dent in the side of his mother's Buick. He watched his father winding transformers and experimenting with electricity in constructing the x-ray machines. This literally sparked his own curiosity with electricity. He blew so many fuses in his father's shop that he ran down to the hardware store and bought his own secret supply of replacements.

Donald wanted desperately to go to public school but his parents would not listen.

"It's a dumb school. I don't learn anything there," he pleaded with his father during his last of many scoldings because of his insolent behavior. His antics had failed to accomplish what he wanted, to be taken out of the parochial school and allowed to attend the public school. One late afternoon he happened on two of his teachers in a compromising situation in the back seat of a car. He described the scene to his parents and from then on he was allowed to attend public schools.

The twenties turned out to be a dichotomy of opposites. World War I was over, people were dissatisfied with the results and tired of the years of sacrifices. Prohibition became the law in 1920 which made it illegal to manufacture and sell alcohol. Since it was not unlawful to consume or drink alcohol it became fashionable to visit speakeasies or carry a pocket flask of gin. The consumption of alcohol soared. Bootleggers were making a financial killing and gangsters fought over territory.

Skilled workers wages had gone up and material prosperity was evident in the cities. Tradesmen drove expensive automobiles. Women were having their hair bobbed and skirts shortened to the knees. But the "Roaring Twenties" had its victims. The farmers were expected to "feed the world" after the devastation of the war in Europe. Some were able to eke out a living, others suffered severely from a sudden fall in the price of produce. California was hit the hardest with not only falling prices, but a severe drought.

Drs. George and Jessie Hare had expected to retire from their medical practices to live comfortably on their investment in the orange groves and vineyards. They were not novices at growing oranges and grapes. They had plenty of knowledge and experience cultivated over years on a small scale. But they had bought in at too high prices and with so little equity. Someone said the Bank of America was the biggest landowner in the state from such foreclosures and as a result it was in financial difficulty.

Both Drs. George and Jessie had to continue practicing medicine to pay their bills. At their advanced ages they found it difficult to maintain a livelihood in a private practice. Dr. George Hare had neglected his practice for his agricultural and land speculation distractions. Dr. Jessie Hare never had a lucrative medical practice as women doctors were not yet widely accepted even by women. Although it was unusual to see a woman in a logging camp high in the Sierras, in desperation Jessie took a job as a company doctor. It was the best she could do to earn money badly needed by the family. The lumber company was fortunate to get her since medical doctors were in short supply right after World War I. She treated all kinds of job injuries, broken and crushed arms and legs, fingers cut off. Some days were grisly. In the summer she took Donald along and he had a job helping the camp cook when he wasn't risking his neck riding logs down a flume. All of the supplies were packed up on mules and Donald was astonished at the amount of grub the woodcutters consumed. He said if the cook ran out of some kinds of food he could get by, but was in for a bad time from the loggers if he ran out of salt.

A MAN'S WORLD

In 1924 Donald Hare graduated from Fresno High School but he could not expect his parents to pay for his college. The silver spoon he was born with had tarnished when his parents lost their investments. Although only seventeen he had grown tall, over six feet, with a slender, athletic build. Tennis was his favorite sport in school. But now he found himself in a man's world so he took a job with the Pacific Telephone and Telegraph Company as a helper to the linemen. After work on payday several of the crew played poker until one had most of the money. They eagerly invited the new kid to join them to fatten the pot. It wasn't long before they found he was not an easy mark. Donald had good card sense. One of his older brothers played cards with him and taught him both poker and bridge. Donald's total recall was an advantage. He had a skill he would use in the future.

Often after work he stopped by the pool parlor and learned to shoot pool and snooker. He developed a smooth stroke with a cue and could hold his own in a friendly game, but stayed away from the hustlers. His mother would never have approved of his even going inside such a place.

After two years he quit the telephone company and enrolled in Fresno State College. He worked in a sandwich shop and took a summer job in the kitchen of a hospital. The breakfast shift started at four in the morning and his first assignment was to shell several cases of eggs and place them on trays for baking in the oven. Breaking them one at a time, he made a mental calculation and realized breakfast for the patients would be ready at ten instead of the customary seven. Quickly he learned how to break two eggs at a time in each hand. Years later, when relating that skill in his early experiences, if someone expressed some doubt he proudly demonstrated he could still do it.

Intrigued with machinery, Donald wanted to know how to operate metal working tools so he enrolled in a shop class. The first day the elderly German teacher handed him a blob of bronze and a file.

"Make me a cube," was his only instruction.

"You vill learn much. How to use your tool, how to measure and above all, patience."

It wasn't exactly what he expected, but he survived the initial project and moved on to learn metal machining.

One summer Donald managed to get a job on a tramp steamer as the ship's radioman for a trip to Hawaii and return. He had known Morse code since he was twelve.

After two years at Fresno State he went back to the telephone company for a year and that convinced him he wanted a college education. It took courage for him to quit his job when men were being put out of work all over the country. 1930 was the beginning of a country-wide depression and the second one in the past ten years for the state of California. Hundreds of banks closed, the unemployed couldn't pay grocery bills and many were evicted from their homes for non-payment of rent or mortgages. At age twenty-three Donald decided his future would be brighter with a college degree than with the skills he acquired climbing poles and splicing wires.

Stanford was his choice. He arrived in Palo Alto with $50 in his pocket and took a job making sandwiches. Hare's success playing poker with the linemen sparked the idea that poker winnings just might be a source of income. With them he paid for his Model A. He walked by the fraternity houses trying to make a decision which one to join. The cars parked in front of the Alpha Tau Omega attracted him. He paused and admired a Stutz Bearcat, then on to the Pierce Arrow with the big headlights on the fenders. The Lincoln with the greyhound on the radiator wasn't as flashy but it conveyed opulence. Donald spent more time admiring the old Model T with its three pedals on the floor, the spark and throttle levers on the steering column. After he gave up the horse and buggy Donald's father used a Model T to make house calls and drive out to his vineyard.

The economic wealth parked in front of the ATO house clearly influenced Donald to pledge to that fraternity.

"No evidence here of a depression," he thought as he went inside to see about becoming a pledge. The mere mention that his father, mother and older brother were medical doctors assured his acceptance into the brotherhood. None of Donald's new associates had an inkling of his precarious financial condition. To them he was just another rich kid from a family of doctors.

23

No sooner had he unpacked his clothes and the ukulele than he learned about the weekly poker game. Not wishing to appear anxious to join the game, he spent his time at the nearby pool table, showing no interest in the chatter about the game about to get started.

"Hey, Hare. You play poker?" asked the one with the card deck in his hand.

Donald walked around the end of the pool table, leaned down to line up his next shot. "Played it some with my brother. Just for matches," he replied as he made his shot.

"Wanna join us?"

"I guess. If it's not too expensive."

"We have a dime limit on raises."

Donald put his pool cue in the rack on the wall and joined the five poker players.

Most of Donald's previous poker-playing experience was with the same individuals from whom he learned their habits, their responses to good cards, bad cards, raises and calls. Also he played with men who were somewhat equal in financial status to whom winning and losing had about the same importance. This group had more diversity. Several came from very wealthy families conspicuous by the clothes they wore and the cars parked out front. He had no way of knowing for sure, but winning was probably more important to him than any others at the table. The first few games were going to be critical. He couldn't be too greedy or they might not let him play. Still, he needed a few dollars every week. The Saturday night job playing the ukulele in a college dance band didn't pay enough to cover tuition.

In the next few months Donald Hare learned much about his poker playing buddies. Roger, the owner of the Stutz and son of a coffee importer, stayed in every game, raised only when he had almost a sure winning hand.

George, who liked to be called "Gib," paid little attention to what was going on and had to be reminded when it was his turn to bet. He was usually late because of his promotional job driving a Model T around town advertising Bank Night and free china for a local theater.

Gabe frequently went against the odds by drawing to an inside straight and revealed his bluffing by clenching his teeth, causing his jaw bones to pulsate. His father was a railroad executive.

Tony was the cautious one, folding more often than anyone and conservative with his raises. His banking family lived in Palo Alto and Tony had the use of the family car only on weekends.

Andy was probably the best player in the group. He knew when to fold, when to raise and seldom lost unless he had a run of bad cards. He owned the Lincoln Phaeton. His parents were in the oil business in the southern part of the state.

Several others joined the regulars, occasionally bringing with them some "outside money." Donald Hare managed to win several dollars a week without being tempted to go for a big kill which he felt could jeopardize the future of the games.

One day near the end of the first year when Donald returned to the frat house there was a note in his mail box. "Please report to the Dean's Office at your earliest convenience." He immediately headed for the administration building. When he entered the dean's outer office he soon found it was not just one of the girls in the office who wanted to see him, but the dean himself, George Bliss Culver. Donald wondered what the dean could want with him. His grades were all passing. He smarted off a little to that assistant instructor he thought was stupid, but that wasn't important enough to have been reported to the dean. Maybe he's going to offer me a job, starting to think a little more positive. For twenty minutes he sat in the outer office before being called into the dean's inner sanctum.

"Mr. Hare, have a seat," the fifty-five-year-old dignified gentleman said, motioning to a chair as he looked over his spectacles.

Donald sat in the chair facing the Dean's desk.

"I am sure you wonder why I have called you in so I will get right to the point. I have it on good authority you are very proficient at cards, especially poker."

Donald gulped.

The dean continued. "I have received complaints from a number of parents that their sons have consistently lost their monthly allowances in the weekly games at the ATO house. Don't misunderstand. No one is accusing you of cheating. You are just a better player than your fraternity brothers." The dean took on a more stern countenance. "Either you stop it immediately or I shall have to ask you to leave the university. Do I make myself clear?" The dean was firm.

Donald was not expecting this and had no prepared defense. "But Dean Culver, I didn't start the games. They have been going on for a long time. I was just asked to join them. Sure I win a few dollars, so do some of the others."

"But I have it on good authority you are the consistent winner. I repeat, if you continue to play poker I shall have to ask you to leave the university."

Donald was a member of the Debating Society and relished the competition it provided. He had a good record for winning debates but he quickly realized he was on the losing side this day.

"Yes, sir," Donald answered and left hurriedly.

This put a big dent in his finances. He didn't want to go back to the sandwich shop nor to the cafeteria where many students worked for meals. Finding a job that paid money to students was almost impossible with unemployment so prevalent. Some students had to leave because their parents could no longer afford to keep them in school. Playing in the dance band alone wouldn't pay for his tuition. Perhaps he could get a job as a waiter in the resort nearby. It catered to a wealthy clientele so the tips might be generous. Yes, that was worth a try.

Donald put on a white shirt, his only bow-tie which he thought would be appropriate for a waiter and headed for the resort. He parked his Model A Ford in the gravel parking lot next to the guests' expensive cars and walked along the flagstone path past the clay tennis courts to the main entrance. No sign of a depression here. The Spanish style covered portal flanked with perfect specimen shrubs smacked of luxury. Passing a glass door to a room that appeared to be a sun parlor he heard female voices and laughter which caused him to pause a second, and look in. The women were playing bridge. This immediately ignited his creative instincts so instead of applying for a waiter's job he asked to see the activities director.

The youthful director sized up this lanky Stanford student as Donald made his pitch for teaching bridge to her residents. She was impressed by his neat appearance which was essential for him to fit into the opulent atmosphere so important to the reputation of the resort. The fact that he could recite Ely Culbertson chapter and verse made only a small impression on her since she knew nothing about contract bridge. The ladies would have to decide.

The young lady led him to the sun parlor, interrupted the games in progress and introduced Donald Hare to the ladies. They did not mind the distraction. Donald turned on the charm, which came naturally for him around women, and expounded on his knowledge of bridge and willingness to share his skills with them. The atmosphere was perfect. Here was a captive group of well-to-do women, most of them married, with time on their hands. The husbands were on the golf course or away making the money to pay for these boring but socially correct surroundings. What better way to learn more about bridge than in the company of this young Stanford student? He was accepted and many looked forward to his regular visits.

For Donald it was perfect. He set his own hours to fit in with his classes. The teaching was flexible, lessons for the beginners and playing for a penny a point for the experienced. It paid better than the poker in the fraternity house. The Dean had done him a favor. That summer he went back home to Fresno with $500 and a used Buick.

When he finished his AB degree in science in 1931 he met with his second economic disappointment. The country was in the midst of the Great Depression and he could find no work as a graduate science major. Detroit auto workers and dust bowl farmers alike emigrated to California looking for non-existent jobs. Those lucky enough to get work as fruit and vegetable pickers made as much as $40 a month during the harvest season.

In later years Dr. Hare said, "I really don't deserve much credit for deciding to do graduate work. I was making more money staying in school, working as an assistant instructor and playing bridge with the ladies than I could taking a job. In fact, I couldn't even get a job."

During his graduate school days Hare was inspired by the research of J. Robert Oppenheimer at the University of California and the California Institute of Technology and his approach to theoretical physics. Hare said Oppenheimer was one of the most intelligent men on the planet. He listened to his lectures at every opportunity and read his papers. They both shared a love of good music. One day Hare happened to get on the same elevator with Oppenheimer and another scientist who were having a conversation. "They were so far above my head I felt like a blithering idiot," Hare said later.

THE TEXAS YEARS

With his Ph.D. completed, except for his thesis, it was time for Donald Hare to leave the university. Actually, he didn't want to leave. He liked teaching. But his recalcitrant attitude at times had not endeared him to some of the higher tenured faculty, resulting in a non-offer of employment. The department secretary worked many hours typing his résumés. But she didn't mind; she had a crush on Donald. Of the 300 mailed he received only three opportunities for interviews. His first job was at Reiber Laboratory in California doing geophysical research. A year later Alexander Wolf, manager of the Geophysical Laboratory of the Texas Company, hired Dr. Donald Hare to head his research group. A full-time research department was a new innovation for Texaco, started in 1929 with three employees and three pieces of shop machinery. This activity was so new it commanded little respect and would have to prove its worth in results. Space for the department was made in a frame warehouse that had been used mainly for the storage of heavy oil field equipment such as motors, valves, pipe and pumps. There were plenty of windows for ventilation in the summer, but it was poorly lit with a few lights and reflectors hung from the rafters of the gable roof. Unheated, the building took on the effects of the outside temperature which could be quite cool when a "norther" passed through the Houston area. The less than ceiling high partitions around the research area were little protection from the dusty winds that frequently penetrated the building when the warehouse doors were opened. The edge-grained wood block floors, designed to minimize damage to equipment that might be dropped or pushed around became oil-soaked over the years, and were difficult to keep clean.

Now that he was finally employed at a real job he felt he could take on the responsibilities of a family. He married Betty Bloom in 1938, a graduate of Scripps College.

Geophysical Laboratory of the Texas Company, 1929

In spite of the elemental conditions in the research area, with cold hands in winter and sweaty palms in summer, the research group made great strides developing devices for the petroleum industry. Additional machinery and laboratory equipment was purchased and the staff increased. They were fortunate to have a number of skillful machinists who could construct anything that was put on paper. Even very simple components such as bolts and nuts had to be fabricated because of the failure of some suppliers during the Depression. Dr. Hare was no stranger to machining methods and had a great admiration for the skill of a talented machinist. The expertise of the two machinists he worked with during graduate school in the basement shop at Stanford taught him the fine points of metal work. He once said, "You can usually tell a lot about the ability of a machinist by looking in his tool box. It will probably be an oak Gerstner and contain handmade tools and jigs and well-cared-for measuring instruments."

The ability of the group to build its own designs was very important to keep the work confidential. Little outside work was contracted to keep the competition from learning the direction of the research. And the orientation of the research was obviously influenced by Dr. Hare's previous work at Stanford with his advisor, Professor Paul Kirkpatrick. Dr. Hare continued the basic research of x-ray polarization and scattering; high efficiency photon counters; industrial application of gamma rays; and industrial electronics. Using this knowledge and perhaps contributing to the state of the art in nuclear physics employing gamma rays and neutrons, devices were developed to improve the search for oil and gas. Little did he realize that many of his efforts would also benefit mankind in medical science and eventually in the defense effort of World War II. He had come a long way since, as a teenager, watching his father constructing his own x-ray machine.

In his four years at the Texas Company Dr. Hare's research resulted in a total of 29 patents. "The patent attorney often looked over my shoulder to see if I had something that should be patented," he said. "Even followed me to the john." He was being facetious. As soon as a device was developed and well documented it was given to an intellectual property group at another location which processed it for registration, leaving the research group to focus all its energies on scientific work. Eleven of the patents were for the improvement of the Geiger-Müller detector counter that had been the standard instrument for detecting gamma rays. By changing the interior design of the device, such as adding disks arranged in parallel to increase the surface in the detector, Hare was able to make it more sensitive and accurate to the intensity of the radiation by a factor of 32. A second re-design made it more rugged for use in the oil fields. He made a further refinement by adding an electrical circuit that would quench rapid pulses so they could be counted effectively, amplified thousands of feet down in the well and transmitted to recording and measuring equipment on the surface. To determine the radioactivity of earth formations traversed by a bore hole, multi-wired instruments were lowered into the hole to transmit data back to the surface. Because of the weight of the cables and its many brass connectors which were subject to corrosion, the procedure was time-consuming and subject to inaccuracies. He was able to design a circuit needing only two wires, with few or no connectors, to power the unit and carry the data to the surface, saving time and increasing accuracy.

A detection device was mounted in an annular chamber of pipe mounted just above the drill bit and connected electrically to the surface, recording the natural radioactivity of the earth formations as the hole was being bored. The detector had to be cushioned and well-protected against the harsh environment above the drill bit. With this device there was no need to stop the drilling and lower an instrument into the well. To reduce the time it took to log a bore hole for radioactivity through formations, he designed a device with many detectors that would send back signals of different frequencies to the recording equipment as each of the detectors passed through the earth formations.

When a well was at the depth to be put into production, the sides of the lower end of the pipe were perforated to let in the oil. At this time a gun perforator was lowered to the bottom of the pipe. The device contains ten or so bullets to be electrically fired simultaneously in a random pattern, piercing the wall of the pipe. The normal procedure was for the operator to lower the gun to the bottom of the hole and then lift it a short distance. Often the gun would be lowered as deep as two miles. The gun, plus the weight of a long column of borehole mud, and the weight of the cable, is a heavy load. This resulted in an unknown amount of cable stretch which resulted in the operator unsure when he had lifted the gun off the bottom of the hole. Dr. Hare devised an electrical circuit connected to an inertial member that would close the circuit and send a signal when the gun was off the bottom. It also sent a signal if the gun should hang up on the side of the hole before it reached the bottom. The electrical circuits had to be carefully isolated to prevent an inadvertent firing of the gun at some undesirable point along the pipe.

Almost constantly in the oil business it is necessary to know the level of a liquid in a large tank or vessel. Glass gauges are sometimes not appropriate where high temperatures and pressures are encountered or the liquid is so viscous it clogs the gauges. Where the liquid is inflammable a float having electrical connections inside the tank is hazardous. Dr. Hare designed a device that could be placed on the outside of the tank, emit radiation and by measuring the scattering of the rays it determined the level of the liquid.

Frequently it is necessary to cement a considerable portion of a bore hole. This is usually done by forcing the cement under pressure down the pipe so that it flows from the bottom up around the outside of the wall between the pipe and the earth formation. His device called for the addition of borax, an easily obtained and inexpensive compound, to the cement. Other alternatives were the addition of radioactive substances such as pitch-blend, carnotite or other ores which emit penetrating gamma rays. These are not readily available at most sites and are more expensive. The Boron in the borax additive in the cement causes slow neutrons to be absorbed in the cement, so when the detector is lowered in the casing it will immediately register a decrease in slow neutrons when it is opposite the cement. Therefore, knowing the depth of the instrument in the hole, the position of the top of the cement is known. This method was found to be less time-consuming and more accurate than a previously used thermometric procedure.

During the refining process of hydrocarbons it is necessary that the specific gravity of the fluids be monitored and controlled continuously even if the liquid is at a high temperature, under pressure or flowing through a pipe. Sampling is not always possible nor desirable. By transmitting radiation through the wall and measuring the scattering of the radiation with a detector, the specific gravity of the fluid in the vessel or passing through the pipe could be determined.

Frequently water enters a bore hole and it is necessary to know exactly where the water entered. The fluids at this time are not just water, but also drilling mud and oil, so lowering any device into the fluid just agitates the latter so that any determination of the entry point could be highly inaccurate. He designed a closed elongated container to be lowered to the approximate level of the supposed water sand and allowed to be held stationary until the fluids have reached a state of equilibrium. With the container remaining stationary, the device inside which is capable of detecting water is moved vertically through the container from one end to the other. As the device travels it sends a continuous record electrically up to the surface. Since both the position of the container and the position of the device inside are known, an interpretation of the data leads to a very accurate location of the water entering the hole.

Another device was invented to measure the thickness of a pipe, tubing or tank with access to only one outside wall. Other methods for doing this, such as x-rays or gamma rays and certain types of electrical or magnetic methods required that both sides of the wall be accessed. Other systems such as the aural method conducted by an expert under certain conditions on limited applications could render a good deal of accuracy. Hare's device worked on all thickness' where only one wall was accessible and yielded accurate information of not only the thickness but also the condition of the walls. By controlling the direction and amount of penetrating rays and measuring the scattering of the radiation the device could be calibrated to indicate the thickness of the material.

Dr. Hare developed several devices for subsurface prospecting. In the search for hydrocarbons it is necessary to know the type of soil formations through which the bore hole is passing. The taking of continuous core samples or side wall samples is very slow and expensive. Another method measured the natural radioactive background of the formation but has not been proven sufficiently reliable. A third method was to run an electrical survey of the natural radiation in the formation but it could not be used in bore holes with the steel casing. This new device which contained a source of highly energetic penetrating particles such as fast neutrons was lowered into the hole. Encased in the same container was a detector shielded from the source of the neutrons so it would record only those that scattered into the formation and returned. The detector was connected to a recorder at the surface. Two models were made, one for cased holes, another for uncased.

In one similar device for subsurface prospecting to increase the energy of the fast neutrons he added either thorium or uranium fertile materials to a mixture of radium and beryllium thus producing some nuclear fission. Knowing how the presence of other elements in the formation affect the scattering of the neutrons, as detected and recorded, revealed important information about the type of formations in the search for hydrocarbon oil sands.

While the research was directed mainly at oil and gas exploration and the related problems of drilling and bringing wells into production there were many discoveries that led to advances in science of other fields. The in-house publication of Texaco, The Texaco Star, printed the following:

HIGH SENSITIVITY RADIATION DETECTOR FOR CANCER RESEARCH

"Dr. D. G. C. Hare, then a Texaco scientist, interested in radioactivity, believed a more sensitive instrument than the Geiger-Müller detector was possible. The 'pick-up' field of the Geiger-Müller detector was restricted to a cylinder. This problem was solved by increasing the field through extension of the 'pick-up' surface. The field was extended by introducing disks in the cylinder. The larger surface picks up more gamma rays, and is therefore more sensitive."

"As far as cancer research is concerned, the result is that smaller, and hence safer, quantities of radioactive iodine is being used in a thyroid cancer diagnosis or treatment, a smaller amount can be injected into the patient, and the sensitive detector is able to pick up the radiation."

"The same principle has been applied to solve industrial problems. Texaco's 'Penetron' is an instrument which rapidly and accurately measures the thickness of pipes, and vessels and their contents, without damage to the material being inspected. The 'Penetron' makes such measurements by means of reflected gamma rays. Since the detector is so sensitive, non-harmful amounts of radioactive elements can be used."

(Texaco gave this technology to the Sloan-Kettering Institute for Cancer, New York.)

The research personnel was increased which called for a new and modern quarters for the laboratory. Dr. Gerhard Herzog, a scientist of many accomplishments, joined the group in 1940. The Texas Company pursued a policy of hiring young graduate engineers fresh out of college. One of them was Roy Mazzagatti, an electrical engineer from Texas A & M. After eleven months in the field working with an exploration team he was transferred to the research group in Houston.

Only a few days on the job, he was taken to a site and given instructions to record voltage data from a gamma ray counter. The next day the data was shown to Dr. Hare who at first was pleased with it until he discovered one element was missing.

"What is the distance from the source to the counter?

"I didn't measure it," replied the young engineer. No one had told him to make this measurement.

Dr. Hare admonished him severely as the rest of the data was worthless without the knowledge of that critical measurement.

Roy had taken military training and respectfully took the criticism from his boss without making any excuses. When Dr. Hare finished his castigation he walked over to the Coke machine, bought two bottles and handed one to the young engineer. Then Dr. Hare apologized for being so hard on him.

Roy was single, in good health, registered for the draft and was ready to go into the Signal Corps. Dr. Hare didn't want to see the young man's education and ability wasted in the Army. He called him into his office.

"I've made an appointment for you to talk to a professor over at Rice who is recruiting engineers for a special project. I want you to talk to him," said Dr. Hare.

Roy didn't know what he was getting into but he suspected he would be headed for either Oakridge or Los Alamos.

A few hours later Dr. Hare returned from a conference with Dr. Larry Scholl in the Texaco headquarters in downtown Houston. Dr. Scholl was Chief of the Geophysical Division of the Producing Division.

"Don't keep that appointment I made for you. The Chief just chewed me out. He said to let them do their own recruiting. We don't want to lose you and we'll put in for a deferment," Dr. Hare explained to Roy.

"Dr. Hare was the smartest man I ever worked with," Roy said, "And I've worked with a lot of smart men. He did more to affect my career than anyone. Every morning he would come in with a new idea on how to use gamma rays or how to beat Black Jack at Las Vegas. And he was the best baseball pitcher our team ever had."

Geophysical Laboratory staff increased to 33 and moved into the newly constructed modern quarters at Bellaire in the Spring of 1940. The painting room, machine shop and seismic truck fabrication were located separately in an "L" shaped building. Of masonry construction it was air-conditioned and well lighted with large, high-wattage fixtures. It provided a clean, bright environment for research.

In April, Dr. Hare's son, Stephen George Corkhill Hare was born. Six months later the disturbing incidents in Europe shaped the future activities of Dr. Hare as for most Americans.

Geophysical Laboratory of the Texas Company, 1941

A CALL FOR DEFENSE

The events of 1939 and 1940 changed the lives of all Americans. Hitler took Poland, Britain and France declared war on Germany. Russia invaded Finland. Germany conquered Belgium, Luxembourg and the Netherlands in a matter of few weeks. Italy declared war on Britain and France. Roosevelt asked Congress for the largest defense budget ever and promised no American boys would ever be sent to fight on foreign shores. Our factories started producing tanks, aircraft and armaments at a rate never thought possible. Britain spent billions in the United States for armaments. Its funds were almost exhausted when Roosevelt devised the "Lend Lease" and asked for a budget of seven billion dollars. Germany responded with the announcement that ships of any nationality sending aid to Britain would be torpedoed.

In 1940 Donald Hare was loaned by the Texas Company to the National Defense Research Committee, which was under the direction of Columbia University. First he was assigned to the U. S. Navy Underwater Sound Laboratory in New London, Connecticut. A few months later he was made director of a new operation, Airborne Instrument Laboratory, New York, a division of the National Defense Research Committee. The cadre was recruited nationwide by Columbia University, offering young electrical engineers or technicians, most of them working at radio stations, an opportunity to be creative in their field and avoid the draft. One of those was Harry Jacobs, a young engineer with the National Broadcasting Company in San Francisco who, years later would become an important player in the life of Dr. Hare. Al Isberg, a television engineer for NBC's experimental television station W2XBS, received a letter from W. B. Lodge, Associate Director of Airborne Instrument Laboratory, and formerly Chief Engineer of CBS, urging him to ask for a leave of absence from NBC as they needed his services immediately. To protect the security of the program, the letter referred to "developmental work on a phase of war research" and "great urgency of our work" and that he was wanted to join the scientific staff. The co-inventor of the transistor, Walter H. Brattain, along with Hector Skifter, Don Miller, Bob Schultz and Orrin Towner, all electrical engineers, joined the effort. This was a collection of the country's best brains in the electrical field.

In spite of U. S. Navy convoys the large German submarine fleet played havoc with cargo ships carrying needed supplies to England. Frequently the ships were surrounded by a wolf pack of eight or ten or even up to twenty U-boats. More than 100 merchant ships and one U.S. warship were sunk in 1942. Not only were subs sinking ships headed for England, but tankers moving oil and fuel for our own domestic use were prime targets along the Atlantic Coast and in the Caribbean. Some automobile service stations on the east coast went out of business because of a shortage of gasoline. The submarines were operating without being challenged along the coast from Georgia to Maine. At times the beaches were littered with pieces of wooden crates and rubber tires that had washed ashore from sunken liberty ships. The ocean horizon at night frequently glowed orange from the flames of a burning vessel.

At that time our methods of reliable submarine detection were virtually zero. Radar and Sonar were then in early stages of development. The Airborne Instrument Laboratory was assigned to develop an airborne detector of submarines operating beneath the surface. Hare was a workaholic in his laboratory and expected a lot from his engineers. His family was living in Connecticut and after a few weeks of a three-hour train commute to New York he took a room in the city and went home only on weekends. Each evening, after dinner, unless he worked late, Dr. Hare walked past the Manhattan Chess Club and paused to look in the window where he saw the members playing chess. It was like a boy looking in a candy store window. He fancied himself a fairly skillful player and was allowed to join the elite club. Although he played there often, it took him over a year before he won his first match. Against a woman.

When the main operations of the laboratory were moved to Mineola, Dr. Hare moved his family nearby. A daughter, Susan, was born.

The urgency of finding a submarine deterrent was always on Dr. Hare's mind. Too frequently he stood on the

47

shore of Long Island watching ships flaming on the horizon, the victims of German torpedoes. His frustrations were later evident in his final report:

"During the first year, the work was very largely of an experimental nature in which various methods of achieving the desired results were suggested, investigated, tested and, in general, discarded. Toward the end of this first year, the basic principles of the final successful equipment developed under this contract were becoming recognized and at the end of the year, the first prototype models were available."

The most promising method of detecting submerged submarines from aircraft was to measure the distortion of the earth's magnetic field caused by the presence of the ferro-magnetic mass of the submarine. There were many obstacles. The amount of distortion is a minute quantity, a vector field is involved since both the submarine and aircraft are moving, and so the direction of the field had to be neutralized or the motion stabilized. Spurious signals caused by the aircraft were a serious problem.

Dr. J. T. Tate and Dr. L. B. Slichter conferred with the British, who had developed a two-coil gradiometer system that under favorable conditions could detect a submarine at a range of 200 feet, which was considered inadequate. Both Bell Laboratories and California Institute of Technology worked on the two-coil device to reduce the background noise caused by its mounting system until November, 1941, when it was terminated because of the more satisfactory tests of the equipment developed primarily by Victor Vacquier, a scientist at Gulf Research and Development

The basis for such an instrument had been worked on in the 1930's by C. W. La Pierre of General Electric. It was called a *flux gate* magnetometer and further research on the device was continued by Vacquier at Gulf Research and Development. He joined the group under Dr. Hare and subsequently a device was put together called the Mark I magnetic airborne detector (MAD). It was mounted in the hull of a PBY airplane and could detect S-type submarines at altitudes of more than 400 feet. Many problems still existed. Reduction of noise sources, deperming hard steel members of the aircraft and stabilization of the magnetically erected gyroscope were necessary improvements. Dr. Hare stated that the work of Victor Vacquier in compensating for the anomalous magnetic fields and noise reduction due to eddy currents was one of the most fruitful efforts of the project.

About the first of January, 1942, a Vacquier Mark I was installed in a blimp at the Lakehurst Naval Air Station. Shortly it made a contact with a moving submerged object. The contact resulted in an unsuccessful destroyer attack. During the month of January at least eight contacts were made but could not be accounted for as being wrecks. On January 22 a contact was made which resulted in a very probable destruction of a submarine and another one surfaced after being detected. With this success the Mark I was improved and a new model Mark II MAD put into production followed by the Mark IV-B. Al Isberg's first assignment was to work with Otto H. Schmitt to help develop a Varlstor stabilized 400 cps oscillator for the Mark IV MAD. Al said Otto Schmitt was one of the most brilliant people he had ever known. Lakehurst became a field laboratory for the installation and maintenance of the equipment.

In May plans were made to install the Mark IV-B in thirty B-18 Bombers. A special tail cone housing was developed to house the equipment, and Langley Field in Virginia became another field laboratory. An experimental model called a "Towed Bird" was designed to trail on a wire behind and below the plane like a radio antenna. It had some merit in that it was isolated from the magnetic field effects of the aircraft structure, but the pilots did not like it. It was dropped from further consideration. On Blimps the detectors were installed in blisters, on PBY's in a tailcone or wingtips, on B-18's in a tailcone, and a single cabane was tried on a LB-7. Installation in a B-25 was unsatisfactory because of the design and structure of the aircraft.

The urgency of developing an effective detector and getting it into production was a priority with Dr. Hare and he pushed his people as hard as he could. They started out in a hangar at the Quonset Point Naval Air Station and moved to a TWA Hangar at LaGuardia Airport. That was inadequate so they made a final move to headquarters in Mineola, on Long Island. Development had been farmed out in Pasadena, Pittsburgh, New York, Schenectady, Quonset Point and Boston. Many companies and institutions cooperated in the development, among them Bell Telephone Laboratories, California Institute of Technology, General Electric, and Gulf Research and Development. Headquarters at Mineola did all of the early manufacturing with the production department converting "breadboard" circuits designed by the scientists to service units that could be operated and maintained by relatively inexperienced hands.

After the Pearl Harbor attack on December 7, 1941, the country was on a full war effort. Civilian automobiles were no longer built. Factories of all sorts were converted to making materials for the war. Women were working at manufacturing jobs females had never even thought of before. Gasoline was rationed to three gallons a week and even that might not be available in some places if a tanker had been sunk by a German submarine. All meat and a few other foods were rationed. It took seven points and 61 cents a pound to buy a slice of ham.

A few months after Pearl Harbor the personnel at the Mineola laboratory increased from 25 to 80. A year later there were 117 personnel, of which 34 were scientists and 83 non-scientific employees. Complete units and components were manufactured to get production under way.

Dr. Hare relied on his former Texaco associate, Dr. Gerhard Herzog, to produce consoles in its research laboratory. To obtain units in a hurry, contracts were let to Radio Corporation of America, Geophysical Services, Consolidated Engineering, Altec-Lansing and Gulf Research and Development. A West Coast Laboratory was established at the Alhambra Airport in early 1943. Harry N. Jacobs was sent out there in charge of development. California offered the advantage of good weather, testing grounds in the high desert at Goldstone Lake, and live testing off San Diego with real submarines.

By this time the MAD had been developed to a high degree of sensitivity and stable operation, probably near the ultimate considering the fact that vacuum tubes were used throughout the equipment. The limiting factor in the use of the equipment was now the magnetic aspects of the aircraft. The wingtip installation of the detector placed the equipment in close proximity of a very large non-magnetic surface, the wing; however, it turned out to be a great generator of magnetic fields due to the eddy-current effect which occurred as the craft turned, banked, climbed or in any way changed attitude in the earth's magnetic field. The work at Alhambra Airport, and the testing in the desert and at San Diego, was largely aimed at eliminating these extraneous signals, and thus effectively increasing the sensitivity and range of the system. An eddy-current compensator was designed and patented by Robert I. Strough and Harry N. Jacobs, members of the Alhambra group. (The patent was issued in 1955, some 12 years after the fact!)

Getting units operational called for the training of pilots and technicians in how to use the equipment. A very sophisticated trainer, much like an aircraft flight simulator, was developed by a group in Mineola, including George Izenour and Otto H. Schmitt. Izenour later became well known as the developer of a state-of-the-art stage lighting system, and Otto Schmitt earned fame as inventor of the "Schmitt Trigger," a vacuum tube trigger circuit widely used for many years, and still in use as a solid state adaptation. This trainer was a combination flight simulator, submarine detector and tracker, and automatic bomb releaser. It took up half of a large room at the laboratory and was the most used piece of equipment. The work force at the laboratory trained more than 1,000 service personnel. Both Army and Navy started training courses at Boca Raton, Camp Murphy, Florida and Corpus Christi, Texas.

The new model Mark VI MAD was given an Army-Navy designation -AN/ASQ-1 - AM/ASQ-1A.

When the latest model of the AN/ASQ-1A was ready for demonstration to Vannever Bush, director of the Office of Scientific Research and Development, and five other officials, they were to be taken for a ride in the lab's Grumman Goose. The Goose is an eight-passenger amphibian aptly named. On a previous trip Al Isberg and the plane's pilot had flown into Roosevelt Field from Quonset Point, R. I., in a very heavy rainstorm against headwinds. When they landed the pilot was disturbed that they had almost run out of gasoline so he requested that the mechanic check it over. The engines were checked and found to be O. K. for the next trip.

For the demonstration they had one problem. With the pilot and Dr. Hare in the co-pilot's seat (he liked to fly the plane when it was in the air) the six dignitaries and Isberg to operate and demonstrate the equipment, they were overloaded. Since it was to be a short trip they reduced the fuel load by 25 gallons to compensate for the weight of the extra passenger. Al had to crouch down in the aisle to operate the new detector model.

The engines were revved up and they started down the runway. The Goose was never a plane to leap into the air under ideal conditions. It rolled down the runway for a long distance, the props in noisy low pitch, the landing gear shocks thumping as the wheels ran over irregularities in the concrete. Using every bit of the runway, the Goose staggered into the air just in time to clear the hangar roof by a scant twenty feet! Dr. Hare turned to Al and shouted, "Isberg, you shouldn't have eaten so much breakfast!"

They flew a few miles east of the New Jersey coast where they knew the location of sunken merchant ships. As they flew near the wrecks the detection equipment reliably recorded their presence. The demonstration was a success. After the group returned to the airport, the pilot and mechanic were determined to find the reason for the difficulty in getting the aircraft airborne. They discovered the hull of the Goose was about half full of rainwater from the previous trip! They didn't bother to tell the guests.

The new detector units were lightweight versions, installed in wing tips of TBF, PBM-3C, OS2U-3, B-24, G-21A, aircraft. In the PBY's alone they had 40 units in service, 24 of which were installed in the tailcone and 16 in the wing tips. The B-18's had 100 installations in service and the Navy Blimps 80. The Atlantic and the Caribbean were being patrolled from Maine to South America. The B-18's were sent to the Eastern Sea Frontier.

The air search for German submarines and the advances of Sonar technology used by the Navy greatly reduced the threat to shipping in preparation for D-Day. Some enemy U-boats escaped destruction, and after E-Day a few sailed into New York harbor flying white flags of surrender. The air patrols were disappointed that they didn't have a chance to engage them before the subs reached safety.

The submarine detection device was not the only development in the laboratory. The engineers were constantly designing improved radio transmitters and receivers and high-powered jamming transmitters for overseas use. Dr. Hare made trips to London to learn first hand what was needed and what was successful.

Developments at Texaco under Dr. Hare's research department were not confined to oil industry devices. The same technology was adapted to a mine detector for determining the locations of non-metallic mines marked with radioactive elements and placed in underground locations. Another type was developed to be mounted on a Jeep or truck. When the vehicle was traveling at ten miles an hour, or slower, the device could signal the presence of a mine, automatically apply the brakes and shut off the engine.

The military needed a quick, nondestructive way to measure the thickness of aircraft propeller blades so it could discover weak spots and thus prevent malfunctions. The shape and various thickness' of the blades made this very difficult, but the gamma radiation methods did it with absolute accuracy. Engineer Roy Mazzagatti was sent to Pratt and Whitney at Dayton, Ohio, to supervise the testing which detected hidden flaws and thus prevented the use of sub-standard propeller blades.

The technique that measured the thickness of a pipe from only one surface was applied to measuring the thickness of large artillery shells. The shell was rotated on rollers next to a detector and the thickness measured quickly and accurately. (From "The Power of Their Vision," E & P Technology Department, Houston, Texas.)

The following is a direct quotation from an introduction to a booklet published for the 36th Reunion of NDRC Division 15, which was involved in Radio Countermeasures (RCM). This was written by Dr. C. Guy Suits, Chief, Division 15 NDRC, General Electric Research Laboratory, Schenectedy, NY:

"Another useful facility that became a part of Division 15 was the Airborne Instruments Laboratory (AIL) based at Mineola, Long Island. This outfit had been a part of Division 6 working on submarine detection methods, and had developed and seen into service the magnetic airborne detector used with some success by the U. S. Navy. But by the end of 1943 that work was complete and AIL had worked itself out of a job. Dr. Donald Hare, in charge of the laboratory, was a very able guy and he had some very able people. And at that time Division 15 was still expanding and as always we were finding it hard to get enough of the right people. So at the beginning of 1944 the AIL laboratory and its entire staff of 180, about a quarter the size of the RRL (Radio Research Laboratory) at that time, was incorporated into Division 15. AIL was given the task of concentrating on countermeasures to the various guided missile systems evolved by the enemy, which were then beginning to become a worry."

"From the European theater we continued to get flaps from time to time and we tried to deal with these as and when they came in. One I remember concerned the VI flying bomb, which they started firing at London in the summer of 1944. Within a few days an unexploded example had been examined and it was found that azimuth guidance was by means of a magnetic compass controlling a gyro, which operated the rudder via a servo system. How could such a system be countered? Obviously not by normal radio countermeasures techniques. The problem was passed on to Don Hare and his team at AIL and they figured out a way that was absolutely fantastic. Their idea was to form a magnetic loop employing existing railway lines, suitably interconnected, all the way around London— a circumference of about 60 miles. This loop would be energized with a hefty current to make it into a gigantic magnetic deflector. They worked out a system that would have required something like 1,000 amps DC, to provide the necessary magnetic field to deflect the compass of a flying bomb at 1,000 feet. The power requirement for the system would have been in the order of 20 or 30 mega-watts, which would have meant dedicating quite a large power station to this purpose. The system was very seri-ously considered and design work began on some of the necessary equipment. But in the end nothing came of it - Allied ground forces overran the flying bomb launching sites in northern France and the threat was countered that way. But I think Hare's VI jammer must hold the records, easily, for the biggest and most powerful piece of counter-measures equipment ever to be considered."

The demise of the German wolf pack and the end of World War II was not the end of the value of the airborne magnetometer. Further improvements made it a feasible instrument for finding mineral deposits all over the world.

As many as twenty aircraft owned by private service companies mapped large areas that were inaccessible to conventional ground searches, such as in heavily wooded areas and water. Large iron deposits were located in Penn-sylvania and Ontario. Interpretation of the magnetic read-ings on the charts led also to the discovery of asbestos, sulfur, lead, nickel, copper, gold, titanium and chromium. The aerial magnetic surveys cannot sense the presence of oil directly, but can pick formations likely to contain oil. This method became a very fundamental tool of the industry, especially in jungle areas, desert and the ocean. These magnetic mapping surveys are important to undeveloped countries, allowing them to benefit from the new technology in their search for oil and minerals.

A RETURN TO PEACE

At the end of World War II the mission of the National Research Committee was at an end and Dr. Hare had to consider what direction his career should take. Roger Milliken, then president of the Deering-Milliken Company, a textile manufacturer, decided his company should start up a research activity and looked for someone with the scientific credentials to direct it. This was an innovative idea as the industry had always depended on outsiders for advice and research. An associate of his, Francis G. Kingsley, had known of Dr. Hare's work during the war at Airborne Instruments Laboratory and suggested that Milliken talk to him. After several conversations they agreed on the financial remuneration (which Dr. Hare said was considerably more than he had been making), the scope of his duties and responsibilities. He was made president of the Deering-Milliken Research Trust. Another example of Roger Milliken's management style of keeping his company ahead of the pack occurred in 1978 when bureaucrats in the Carter administration put out the erroneous information that the natural gas reserves of the country were rapidly being depleted. Natural gas for heat was important in the processing of fabrics. To be prepared for any such problem, Milliken immediately purchased electric quartz heaters ready to be installed if needed.

Dr. Hare and his family moved to South Carolina and he soon became familiar with the mechanics of weaving fibers into textiles.

"When I observed that a whole city block of two stories of machines could run almost constantly with the attention of one supervisor, I realized there wasn't much I could do to improve the efficiency. If I were to make a contribution it would have to be mostly in the composition of the fibers," Dr. Hare said, recalling his early days in the textile business.

A short time later he was able to convince Milliken that the mills were no place for him to do his work, that he had to be in the northeast where he could make better technical contacts. He moved to Greenwich, Connecticut and set up his lab in an old empty Masonic Lodge building with his office in a wing with a big arched window and a nice view of lawn, trees and shrubbery. Not one to shun comforts when they were available, during the cool months he made daily use of the large stone fireplace that permeated the room with a warm cozy glow of a wood fire. The environment was pleasant. Dr. Hare recruited a work force which included Norman Armitage, who had both a law and chemical engineering degree. Armitage became a very valuable employee of the company which Milliken recalls as a great contribution of Dr. Hare by bringing the chemist into the organization.

A newly developed polyester filament fiber had one sticky characteristic that posed a problem. The slub (a texture nub in the fabric) appeared at regular intervals rather than at random. Dr. Hare altered the electronics of the process so the slubs occurred at random to create the desired texture of the fabric.

One day a friend of Dr. Hare's just home from the occupation forces in Europe came by and handed him a small sound recorder, "Look what I picked up in Germany. You oughta see what they're doing."

Dr. Hare turned it over in his hands and opened the cover. "Hmm. Tape. This is interesting," he said.

Until then the latest in sound recording was on wire. Bing Crosby financed the start-up of Ampex, which quickly dominated the commercial market. Ampex also discovered the German model but was using the German-made tape. Dr. Hare learned the 3M company had developed a new tape for sound recording which had possibilities. He rebuilt the drives and the circuitry and used the play and record heads from the German machine. The result was a far superior recorder than the Ampex model using the German tape.

"I got twice as good frequency response and signal to noise ratio at 15 inches per second as Ampex got with 30," he modestly exclaimed. The speed of 15 inches per second soon became the industry standard.

He showed the prototype of the new recorder to Sherman Fairchild, whose reaction was, "Make me ten." Anything new was exciting to this man of many talents and vision. Fairchild had just started his newest venture, the Fairchild Recording Company. His first love was photography and he made many experiments with chemicals to make stop-action photos with flash. His most famous first public attempt was at an indoor boxing match at night in Boston. The flash was so bright it blinded the contestants temporarily and the match was stopped for a few minutes. He was asked to leave. The picture was a success and ran in several newspapers. As an entrepreneur he developed an aerial camera and started the Fairchild Aerial Camera Corporation, then developed some flight instruments and changed the name of the company to Fairchild Camera and Instrument Company. He was not satisfied with the inconvenience of taking aerial photos with the available open cockpit airplanes. In 1924 he designed a closed cockpit high-wing monoplane which was predicted to be a failure by experienced pilots who felt one had to hear and feel the wind. It was the forerunner to the Fairchild 24, which was a very successful aircraft. He was the first to add flaps and wing slots, hydraulic brakes and retractable landing gears. The aircraft company made the primary trainer, the PT-19, during World War II. He started two airlines that were later merged into Pan American Airlines. In 1957 he started the Fairchild Semiconductor Corporation to manufacture silicon transistors and electronic components. A few years later Dr. Hare was using some of its products.

Dr. Hare was bored with the research in fibers and excited about the developments in electronics. He could not in good conscience be moonlighting in electronics while on the payroll of the Deering-Milliken Research Trust. Also, Roger Milliken was having second thoughts about having his research so far away from the mills, and Dr.

Hare did not want to move back to the south. It was now time for termination talks with Milliken which were finally culminated and several of the staff moved to South Carolina, adjacent to one of the mills. The research organization of the Milliken company proved to be an important department of the company and continues today.

Now Dr. D. G. C. Hare was again unemployed.

THE D. G. C. HARE COMPANY

In 1949 Dr. Hare moved to New Canaan, Connecticut, and started the D. G. C. Hare Company with almost no capital. Ruth Kuntz, his bookkeeper and girl Friday during his years at the Deering-Milliken research group, agreed to follow him in his new pursuit. Since he couldn't afford to pay her a salary, she lived with him and his family until the company could afford to pay her. She found a location for the new company in part of Farrety's Machine Shop. A concrete block addition was added for some office space. Ruth had triple duty as a secretary, bookkeeper and baby-sitter.

Howard Chinn of the Columbia Broadcasting Company heard about the new recorder Dr. Hare developed and ordered six. Dr. Hare again called his friend Sherman Fairchild.

"Sherman, I've sold six recorders to CBS and I need $10,000 to fill the order."

"Come on over," was the reply.

Fairchild gave him the money which allowed him to hire a big work force of five. Warner Eliot, an electrical engineer graduate of Reed College; Roy Hamme, an electrical engineer graduate of Yale; Ken Bauer, a mechanical engineer and former submariner, also from Yale; and Don Fisher, an electrical engineer, completed the engineering group. Frank Richardson, an experienced technician and purchasing agent, was the fifth new hire. Dr. Hare now was able to pay Ruth Kuntz a salary. This new broadcast quality development had the crew working all night the day before the prototype was to be demonstrated at the New York headquarters of Columbia. Some of the wives joined them to provide food and coffee for the all-night effort. By morning the equipment passed all tests and the engineers went home to get some sleep to be fresh for the afternoon demonstration.

The equipment worked perfectly and the contract was completed. A "lip-sync" device was then developed and added to the broadcast tape recorder.

The National Bureau of Standards gave the company a contract which resulted in the development the first meteor tracking device.

Dr. Hare's marriage became a casualty beginning with his long hours of dedication to work during the war and culminated in a difference of opinion in handling the discipline of the two children. He moved out in 1952 but had no thoughts of divorce.

Dr. Hare's contacts in the recording industry soon opened a new opportunity. In 1946 Hazard Reeves had become involved in a new film projection process that was later to be called Cinerama. The multiple screen projection was invented by Fred Waller, who had the backing of Laurence Rockefeller and Time, Inc. The new association asked Reeves to develop the sound system to go with it and he invented the world's first magnetic stereo sound system. The backers expected the filmmakers in Hollywood to be taken with it, and when they were not, Rockefeller and Time lost interest and discontinued their financial support. Reeves, as much an entrepreneur as engineer, knew a bargain when he saw it. He bought the equipment for only a few thousand dollars. Then Reeves hired physicist, musician and recording sound artist Wentworth Fling to run the company. Fling found Dr. Hare and gave him a contract to build the equipment for the stereo sound synchronized on 35 mm. tape with projection to three wide screens. Speakers were installed behind the screens, on the sides and in the back of the theaters for realism never before attained. Then Reeves, Michael Todd and Lowell Thomas produced five pictures specifically for the new operation in special theaters that grossed over $100 million dollars.

Reeves proceeded to protect his source of equipment for Cinerama by offering to acquire the D. G. C. Hare Company with an exchange of stock. Dr. Hare received 125,000 shares of Cinerama stock for all of the 500 issued shares of Hare Company stock.

Ruth Kuntz's roommate introduced Ruth to Hazel Shaw, a recent college graduate in chemistry who worked for American Cyanamid Corporation. They had a similar avocation. On weekends Ruth often went target shooting with Dr. Hare. Hazel was a member of her company's rifle shooting group. Ruth then introduced Hazel to Dr. Hare and encouraged her to try pistol shooting.

Normally, on a Friday late afternoon Ruth abandoned her office duties while she and Dr. Hare set up the Star reloading tool which measured the powder, set the primer and seated the bullets for the weekend practice or a pistol shooting match. They worked as an experienced team, even casting the bullets. All of this care was necessary to utilize fully the precision of his finely tuned target pistols with their expertly honed and polished workings that resulted in an effortless smooth squeeze of the trigger. He was an expert marksman and had earned many ribbons and medals. He practiced incessantly. In one house he had a range in the basement with targets hung on wires strung on pulleys.

On this one memorable beautiful Saturday Autumn morning in Connecticut the match preliminaries were out of the way, the contestants were lined up at their stations in the Stamford Arsenal when Dr. Hare gave the order to "fire." They all fired at their targets, save one. Hazel Shaw squeezed the trigger. The gun did not fire. She was experienced in target shooting with a rifle but was new at pistol shooting. It was her first match, using an unfamiliar borrowed handgun. She was nervous and had failed to push the clip all the way in. With no cartridge in the firing chamber, the pistol failed to fire. She asked for a restart.

"Absolutely not," was the reply from Dr. Hare. "You are disqualified."

A few weeks later Hazel went with Ruth to Dr. Hare's house. In the excitement of two women visitors his puppy vomited on the rug. Hazel said a man who liked dogs couldn't be all bad. Soon thereafter Dr. Hare and Hazel started dating. The romance had its ups and downs and was subject to the usual barbs about the difference in their ages. Although he had been separated for several years he had not considered a divorce. He made a remark that if he ever got married again it would be to a svelte black-haired Italian ballet dancer. After a year it was obvious that Hazel was ready to end her relationship with him unless he was serious about marriage.

"I think you should learn something about what it's like to work in a small company. It will be different and you may not like it," Dr. Hare advised.

Hazel didn't know beans about office work. She quit her job at American Cyanamid and started to work for Dr. Hare the day Ruth Kuntz went to the hospital for surgery. It was a hectic week until Ruth returned.

During several years of bachelor living Dr. Hare had become what he considered a fairly good gourmet cook. Hazel let it be known she knew nothing about cooking. Her mother always did the cooking and Hazel spent little time in the kitchen. Dr. Hare suggested she take cooking lessons. Again Ruth to the rescue as she located a chef in Greenwich Village in New York City who gave private lessons.

Twice a week Hazel boarded the train to New York City for her cooking lessons. Dr. Hare let her off work early those days. "But he made me pay for the lessons," Hazel said. There was only one other woman in the class so they had individual instruction. The chef was a character, a homosexual, who shaved his arms. Hazel learned the basics of cooking such as how to bone a squab, something every housewife should know. Before the series of lessons was completed the chef left the Village for San Francisco.

"But it gave me confidence. Whenever Donald said I was doing something wrong I could retort, 'that's the way I learned in cooking school,'" Hazel said. After they were married she insisted on having a professional quality Kitchen-Aid Mixer and Waring Blender, which she still owns.

Even after years of separation, filing for divorce in 1956 so he could marry Hazel was probably the most difficult task Dr. Hare ever faced. In business matters he hung tough, but he could not handle emotional personal relationships. For months he postponed going to an attorney. When he finally took the step, he wanted no part of any negotiations. As a result Dr. Hare agreed to a settlement that strapped him financially for many years.

Shortly after the divorce became final, Dr. Hare and Hazel set their wedding date. His son and daughter had known Hazel for some time, but Dr. Hare knew they would be distraught at the thought of his getting married again. Much to his surprise son Stephen took it as a non-event and 13- year-old Susan asked if she could go along on their honeymoon. During the school spring break she did join them in Florida as the newly married couple were there partly on honeymoon and Sonar business with the Navy. This was the beginning of a dual role for Hazel that continued for the rest of their married life. She was homemaker and business associate doing whatever needed to be done from office work to running errands. He seldom made an important decision without quietly running it by her.

Completion of the Cinerama contract left an uncertain flow of business in the fast-changing science of recording multiple channels on wide tape. The Navy gave the company a contract for Sonar trainers. Short term contracts and special orders paid the overhead, but no proprietary product emerged. With the development of the transistor by Bell Labs, vacuum tubes were gradually being eliminated. Dr. Hare was intent on keeping current with the state of the art even though the early devices had limited applications. He had worked closely with Bell Labs during the war. As new devices were developed, one of his friends at Bell gave him a handful of the new transistors. He was as knowledgeable as anyone in the country as this new technology developed. Naval Research gave the company a contract to develop method testing and applications of transistors.

By the end of 1957 the future of the D. G. C. Hare Company was not dismal, but it was struggling for a direction. Dr. Hare had developed the best scientific data recorder in the business, but a growing or even stable demand for it was uncertain. A synchronous-with-film recorder was built for the Columbia Broadcasting System. A contract on transistor circuit development for the armed services briefly occupied some of their engineering development skills.

M. I. T. gave the company a contract for a part of their "Project Lincoln," which resulted in the development of a low frequency multi-signal correlator which could cross-correlate 300 bits of information and distinguish individual signals.

Several engineers, M. I. T. graduates identified as the "Westchester Group," were hired to continue work on an electronic controlled freeway traffic system they had started with a company that folded. Their employment was brief.

Ruth Kuntz was appalled at their lack of basic spelling and manners.

The affiliation with Cinerama did not bring in any new business and the company was still searching for a proprietary product.

A MERGER

The Sangamo Electric Company's president, Chick Lanphier, as a young engineer was personally involved in the development of Sonar for the Navy in World War II. Even though he had risen to chief executive responsible for all operations of the company, much of his time was devoted to new product development and production contracts with the government. Going through his mail after returning from a trip to the Naval Research Laboratory, he scanned a memo from his vice-president in charge of engineering. He picked up his phone, "Slim, who in hell is the D. G. C. Hare Company?"

Ted Leach is a tall, Lincolnesque figure whose posture seemed to almost apologize for his height.

"It's owned by a Dr. Hare who has been designing tape recorders for several years. Had a few contracts with Naval Research and M.I.T. Designed and made the Cinerama sound system. I heard about him from one of my old buddies," Slim answered.

"We could damn well use some smarts in that area. Look into it."

That was enough to send two engineers to see if the Hare Company could supplement their design efforts on the Sonar recorder. Experience had taught most of the executives that the first day back after a trip the boss was usually testy. They did what he said and tried to stay out of his way.

The engineers from Sangamo spent some time going over the developments of the Hare Company but were reluctant to give up any turf to an outside company. With the pressure to deliver a prototype and some sticky problems with the tape transport, they badly needed some of Dr. Hare's expertise. An agreement, part design and part fabrication, was worked out which kept the Hare Company partially occupied for the rest of the year. Both chief executives had frequent engineering conferences and became friends.

One morning in early December Ruth Kuntz, answered the phone, left her chair and opened the door to the shop. "Mr. Lanphier wants to speak to you," she said in the direction of Dr. Hare's work bay.

He returned to his office. "Hello, Chick. What's on your mind?"

"I want to buy your company. Are you interested?" Chick replied in his midwestern accent slightly tainted by his years at Yale.

"Hadn't thought about it. I suppose it's possible. We can talk."

Perhaps selling out to Sangamo might be the smart decision, Dr. Hare thought as he considered how spotty the contracts were, but he didn't want to be negotiating from weakness. "Do they want my business or do they want me?" he asked himself. "Whatever the price, will it be cash or stock?" He picked up the Wall Street Journal and looked up the price of Sangamo stock. "Not cheap. How bad do they want us?" he wondered. Dr. Hare had every respect for Chick Lanphier's intellect and knowledge of electronics, but he wondered how tough he would be in a negotiation.

The Hare company had been going nowhere under Cinerama's ownership and Dr. Hare was sure they would be happy to spin it off and reverse the stock swap, giving the ownership back to him. If he could make a reasonable deal with Sangamo Electric it could benefit both parties.

When Chick arrived they exchanged a few words and immediately went out into the shop. Chick had been there several times before but had not given much attention to the machinery or the personnel.

Paul Faynor was machining a door for a tape recorder.

"He's one of the best at designing a part and making it like a piece of jewelry." Dr. Hare bragged. "He can do it all. We don't have to engineer it, give it a part number and send it to a draftsman before it can be made."

Chick was not all that interested in the machinery or the personnel. He wanted Dr. Hare. They returned to the office.

Chick broke the silence. "If we can get together, here's what I propose. We'll keep the D. G. C. Hare Company as a wholly owned subsidiary. You'll be in complete charge and you can keep your present employees. I don't know what kind of backlog of orders you have, but we can keep you busy with making assemblies and design work ....”

Ruth Kuntz interrupted. “Excuse me. But today is payday, Dr. Hare, and you need to sign the checks.” She smiled and placed the checks in front of Dr. Hare. At first he was a little startled, but realized it was a strategic move of Ruth’s to demonstrate the company was able to meet its payroll.

Dr. Hare signed the checks quickly and passed them back to Ruth. “I dunna know, Chick. I’m a pretty independent bastard, as you well know. We have a similar deal with Cinerama and it hasn’t worked out. I’ll have to undo that and it may cost me. Makes me reluctant to go that route again.”

“But you’ll be completely in charge. Free to make your own decisions. We just want your experience in designing and manufacturing recorders. You will have the assurance and security of the capital of a larger company behind you. We can keep you busy doing what you like to do.”

“I have to sleep on it. We still have to talk about the finances. Here’s a balance sheet and income statement through last month. You can take it with you and we can talk some more.”

Chick made a discernible effort to conceal his surprise that the numbers were not as large as he expected.

Many telephone conversations between Chick and Dr. Hare took place in the next month and it appeared they were close to an agreement pending the yearend financial statements. Cinerama cooperated by giving Dr. Hare back his 500 shares of the Hare company in exchange for the 125,000 shares of Cinerama stock. A deal was finalized on February 19, 1958, in which all of the 500 shares of the D.

G. C. Hare Company were acquired by Sangamo Electric in exchange for 4,918 shares of that company's common stock. The day before, Sangamo stock closed at $33. Dr. Hare and Chick had many oral agreements about the operation of the Hare Company. They trusted each other and felt there was no need to reduce them to writing. Dr. Hare was used to doing business with a handshake. The only signing they did was at the bank to transfer the company account to Sangamo Electric and Dr. Hare delivered the shares of the D.G.C. Hare Company to Chick. These two middle-aged executives were so exuberant about the deal they left the bank skipping down the sidewalk like a couple of first-graders. People stopped and stared.

Chick brought his wife, Signe, on the trip so that evening the Hares and the Lanphiers celebrated the new alliance. After a few drinks the euphoria turned a little wacky as the two men bet on whose young wife had the broadest beam. Signe had brought along some needlework to pass her time on the plane. It was a quilted runner nearly completed. While the men were searching for a tape measure she went into the bathroom and pinned the runner around her hips under her skirt. She won.

For the next year engineers traveled between the two companies, working on designing sophisticated multi-channel tape recorders for the defense department. At times Dr. Hare became extremely agitated when the design engineers at Sangamo Electric covered ground he had explored before.

"Damn it, I told you before I tried that several years ago and it won't work. Why in hell do you insist on spending months and money when all you are going to do is prove me right?" he barked out in an engineering meeting. His impatience for a complete disregard of his empirical information made him a controversial figure and several engineers dreaded to engage him in design discussions.

Late in 1958 Chick asked Dr. Hare to come to Springfield for a conference.

"Donald, I don't have to tell you things haven't been too great lately and we're looking for ways to cut expenses. We have plenty of vacant space and we want to move your operation here. It will result in less travel, less time lost and reduction in overhead." Chick was trying to sell him, but not with conviction it would be successful.

"You will recall we had an agreement that if we were to move the location I could set up my laboratory wherever I chose," Dr. Hare said, "And it sure as hell won't be Springfield, Illinois. You were born here, but I don't like the climate."

The two argued for a while and Chick agreed that Dr. Hare could relocate where he wanted. This set the wheels in motion for Dr. Hare to seriously consider moving the location of the laboratory. His acquaintance from Stanford days, Charlie Litton, had called Dr. Hare and offered to rent him space in his plant in Grass Valley, California. Charlie Litton bought a building that was built to be a hospital during World War II and was never finished or occupied. After he sold a part of his business in San Carlos to "Tex" Thornton he moved the remaining portion of his operation to Grass Valley and continued to make glass blowing lathes for making vacuum tubes. Litton's lathe was the finest made; he shipped models all over the world. The big hospital building was more space than he needed so he was anxious to rent a portion of it.

As a young man Dr. Hare spent many days in the foothills of the Sierras and the thought of going back was so exciting he could hardly wait. He and Hazel flew out to California, drove up to Grass Valley and were taken with it. They returned to New Canaan and Dr. Hare called in his most valuable employees to see how many would relocate with him. Ruth Kuntz, Ken Bauer, Roy Hamme and Paul Faynor all agreed to the move. These were his key people and he was gratified they were willing to make the change.

After a rental agreement was reached with Litton, Dr. Hare called Chick to tell him they were moving to California. Sharing space with Litton was to be temporary and, as it turned out, it certainly was. Even though he didn't have the money to buy any property, Dr. Hare looked around the area for a future permanent location; he even hired a pilot to fly him over parts of the county. On New Year's Day he drove to a spot he had seen from the air, walked up the hill and said, "When I can stand here on New Year's Day in my shirt sleeves, this is the place for me." Grass Valley was a sleepy little town with no industry, except Litton's small operation, since the Empire gold mine closed down during World War II. Prior to the move Hazel Hare flew out to Grass Valley to find suitable housing for the employees. There had been no calls for rental housing in the area and practically none existed. It was almost futile for a while but she managed to find houses around the county for all the employees. For themselves they were able to rent a nice house that belonged to a doctor away on some foreign assignment.

Sangamo Electric moved the plant's machinery and office, including Dr. Hare's oak tables, swivel chair and bookcases with all his technical library. When the move was completed and Paul Faynor had most of the machinery set up and in operation, Dr. Hare made a trip back to Springfield to talk to Chick about their recorder development plans. For some unknown reason he took Litton with him.

It was a large meeting in Chick's corner office. Chairs were brought in from Mr. Funk's office which was next door, connected with a private bathroom and bar between the two. Attending was Chick, of course; Donald Funk, chairman of the Board; Ted Leach, vice-president, engineering; Herb Johnson, chief engineer; Cecil Clark, vice-president, finance; Dr. Hare and Charlie Litton. Donald Funk really didn't have much knowledge about the recorder or what it was supposed to do. Close to retirement age, his whole adult life was spent with the company. He served as the right-hand man to Chick's father and moved up when the elder Lanphier passed away. Funk knew all the people in the utility industry, which was the largest market for the company's products, and the most profitable, for fifty years. Chick always included him in such meetings but really Funk's main interest was waiting for delivery of the new $26,000 Rolls Royce he had ordered on his last visit to the British plant. When he finally got delivery he bought a chauffeur's cap, put it on his head and his wife in the back seat when they went out together.

Litton was just extra baggage in the meeting, but he turned on his charm and everyone present already knew about his skill in designing and making vacuum tubes. It could have been evidence of his frugality, or just being cheap, that appealed to some of the brass. The development program the Hare group would pursue had been discussed thoroughly when Chick, Clark and Funk excused themselves and got together in Funk's office. They decided that perhaps it might be wise to put Litton in charge of the development program. Dr. Hare might be a little too lavish with expenditures and Litton could hold down costs. When the three emerged from Funk's office, Chick had the task of communicating the decision to Dr. Hare.

"Donald, we have decided to put Charlie in overall charge of the development project...."

Dr. Hare jumped to his feet, shoved his chair behind him, almost tipping it over. "Just what the hell gave you that idea? He's a tube designer."

"You'll still be in charge of the technical development. But you don't know anything about finances and we want to keep costs down."

Dr. Hare moved closer to Chick. They were face to face, almost touching. Dr. Hare, red-faced, shouted, "What do you mean I don't know anything about finances? I sold my company twice." Dr. Hare shook his fist. "You can't teach me anything about finances."

A short silence. Cecil Clark thought for a minute there was going to be a fistfight. The others just watched, silently.

Dr. Hare backed away and sat down. "Right now, *Mr. Lanphier*, I suggest you fire me."

"All right, you're fired. But we'll still keep you as a consultant at $50,000 a year.

"75."

"I thought it was 50."

"It just went up."

That ended the meeting. There were no good-bye hand-shakes. Dr. Hare and Litton returned to Grass Valley. Dr. Hare held no animosity toward Litton over this turn of events. Charlie had not solicited the job.

There was another version of what happened at the meeting, but with the same end result. Traditionally, every year when the Sangamo Electric profit numbers were in for the previous year's operation, Chick made a talk to the Sangamo Electric Management Club. This was a group of some 200 middle management and engineering people who met monthly. After reporting on the usual operations for the year he came to the acquisition of the Hare Company.

"As many of you know, a year ago last February we acquired the D. G. C. Hare Company to strengthen design and development of our tape recorders for the Defense Department. Actually, we acquired the company to get the services of Dr. Hare on a full-time basis. Now the cantankerous old fart has quit."

Both Chick and Dr. Hare had a problem. Sangamo owned some machinery in Litton's building, had a few talented people on the payroll there, and Litton really didn't know anything about the sophisticated recorders they were developing. When Litton and Dr. Hare arrived back in Grass Valley, Litton called Chick and said he didn't want the job of overseeing the research and development of the recorders.

THE BIRTH OF THE GROUP

Dr. Hare didn't waste any time after he was fired from his former company. He formed a new corporation called the Grass Valley Group, Inc. The plan was to attract four or five other engineers who wanted to do research and development in the pristine surroundings of the Sierra foothills. Hence the choice of the name: "The Grass Valley Group."

After Litton called Chick and said he didn't want to supervise the development for the recorder division of Sangamo, which formerly had been the Hare Company, Chick tried to patch things up with Dr. Hare.

"I agree it was a mistake to bring Charlie into the picture and we want you to continue as president of the Hare Company."

"Too late, Chick. Remember, you fired me. I just incorporated my new business. It's called the Grass Valley Group We're open for business if you want to give us a development contract. In addition to the consulting fee, that is."

"You won't reconsider?"

"No. Oh, by the way, Chick, have you decided what you're going to do with all that machinery and inventory you own in Litton's place? I could use some of it if the price is right." Dr. Hare had to be smiling.

Sangamo had just paid for moving all of that equipment from Connecticut to Grass Valley, paid millwrights to set up the machinery, relocated a half-dozen employees and had no one to run the company. No one was technically capable of developing advanced state-of-the-art tape drives for use in recording complicated instrumentation. Dr. Hare bought the assets from Sangamo for a song. Now The Grass Valley Group, Inc. had the machinery, the former employees of the Hare company, $12,500 in the bank and no business.

No other scientists joined Dr. Hare in this endeavor and as the business evolved he wished later a different name was chosen. Chick and Dr. Hare patched up their differences and Sangamo gave the Grass Valley Group a development contract.

CINERAMA TO THE RESCUE

Looking for business, Dr. Hare called Wentworth Fling with whom he dealt in manufacturing the sound system for Cinerama. The timing was perfect. Cinerama was going to build some more theaters and gave The Grass Valley Group a contract for $400,000 to furnish more amplifiers. About that time Tony King and Bill Rorden, engineers with Varian Associates in the Bay Area, had heard about Dr. Hare and his new company. They drove up to see about making a change. Dr. Hare agreed to hire them and they both seemed ready to move to Grass Valley. But when Tony King got back home and discussed it with his wife they decided that if they made a change it would be to go back to Canada.

"How about you?" asked Dr. Hare of young Bill Rorden.

"I'd like to come." said Rorden who liked to solve engineering problems and thrived on challenges. He was a Stanford graduate and his talents had been readily recognized at Varian. Promoted to senior engineer, he was a victim of the Peter Drucker principle that people are promoted to their level of incompetence. Bill was not incompetent in making decisions, but he spent too much time with paperwork and in meetings which he disliked. He wanted to be involved personally in the challenge of creating new products and solving problems. Dr. Hare had hired several engineers in his time and worked with many. Rorden was very modest about his qualifications, tending to be quiet, and shy. Actually, during the interviews Dr. Hare was more impressed with Tony King. When King turned down the job Dr. Hare was glad Rorden accepted because he needed an engineer. Dr. Hare quickly recognized he had hired a very bright young engineer who could be very important to the progress of the company.

It took a while for Dr. Hare to find out how well rounded this shy young man was. Bill Rorden didn't spend all of his time designing electronic circuits. He flew gliders, had a pilot's license and owned an airplane. They shared the same attraction for flying, but Dr. Hare never bothered to get a license.

The company had just started manufacturing the big order from Cinerama for more amplifiers. Dr. Hare briefed Rorden on the first equipment the Hare Company manufactured a few years earlier in Connecticut. The new young engineer studied the circuit schematics and the improved prototype amplifier he and Roy Hamme had developed using solid state components. Wentworth Fling of Cinerama made several trips to the Grass Valley Group and approved of the new circuit design with solid state components. On one trip Fling stayed too long and was going to miss his flight back to New York if he had to drive to the airport.

They called the airline, and it delayed departure for a short time while Rorden flew Fling to Sacramento.

The very first units built by the Hare Company back in Connecticut consisted of vacuum tube circuits because the development of transistors had not progressed far enough at that time for use in anything except simple electrical applications such as driving speakers or electric motors. The new models of solid state components were so much better that Cinerama decided not only to use them in its new theaters, but planned to replace all the older equipment. Dr. Hare knew development engineers at Bell Laboratories who kept him informed and gave him samples of the newest transistors. By 1960 many types were available on the market. Dr. Hare and Roy Hamme were probably two of the most knowledgeable people in the country on the application of solid state components. Rorden converted his knowledge of tube circuits and microwave technology to solid state which he soon used extensively in designing audio equipment for the radio and television broadcast industry.

A CHANGE OF ADDRESS

However well intended it was at the start, sharing facilities for the two companies in Litton's building led to minor but frequent confrontations and created tensions between Dr. Hare and Charlie Litton. When Litton complained that the Grass Valley Group employees were using too much toilet paper and paper towels, Dr. Hare thought Litton was just being cheap. Litton even had an employee separate the sheets of the 2-ply towels so they would go twice as far. Tensions mounted. These two engineers were highly opinionated personalities with short fuses. All hell broke loose when Litton laid off a worker who Dr. Hare thought would be good in his company and hired him. Litton accused Dr. Hare of hiring away one of his employees and the sparks flew. A friendship that dated back to Stanford days ended abruptly. The two longtime friends never spoke to each other again.

Almost no buildings were available in Grass Valley or nearby Nevada City, but Dr. Hare was determined to move immediately. The only building they could find was a very run-down vacant structure that had been a processing plant for freezing chickens. The movers were called and worked over the weekend moving the Grass Valley Group. One of the machines was too big to go through the door so a hole was cut in one wall.

The Cinerama order was completed with an after-tax profit of $120,000. Now Dr. Hare could buy that property he discovered when he hired a pilot to fly him over the area. It was an ideal 80 acres. From the road it rose gradually and then steeply to the very back, high enough for a splendid view of the Sacramento Valley, and above the winter cloud layer that sometimes hung over the valley. A previous owner apparently had planned some construction and leveled an area that was perfect for a building pad. The price was $500 an acre which Dr. Hare thought was too much, especially since it had no frontage on the road. Dr. Hare bought three acres along the road right in front of the 80 he wanted. He put out the word he was starting a chicken ranch. The price of the 80 acres came down to less than $300 an acre. A Peninsula area architect visited the site and designed a functional, 4,000-square-foot building made of split-blocks with a face that resembled stone. The structure blended with the natural beauty of the sloping ground in the midst of large Ponderosa Pines and next to a small lake. It was built for a cost of only $40,000, with Bill Rorden doing most of the wiring. There were two small luxuries. A small private bathroom off Dr. Hare's office and below his window overlooking the lake, and an interior wall covered with white, gold-bearing quartz rock from the Empire mine. An "A" frame house was built for Dr. and Mrs. Hare so he could be on the property full time. It was located well above the plant, somewhat secluded by the forest of pines and firs.

As industrial sites go, this one was primitive. No piped in water, no sewer and only single phase electric power along the road supplying electricity to the ranches in the area. Dr. Hare wanted three-phase to run the machinery and made such a request to the power company. They replied it would cost $30,000 to run it from Highway 20 down Bitney Spring Road to the plant. Dr. Hare "screamed like an eagle" and threatened to file a complaint with the utility commission on behalf of himself and ranchers along the road. A few days later, power company trucks with their big reels of wire could be seen along Bitney Spring road with linemen on the poles stretching the fourth wire.

Fortunately there was a natural spring on the property which had a flow more than adequate for the present plant and future expansion. Dr. Hare made a collection box, installed a pump and piped water up to a newly constructed redwood storage tank. The tank, located on an elevation 100 feet above the plant, provided plenty of head pressure for the building and ran an array of RainBird sprinklers that watered the shrubbery and lawns. The area receives 60-70 inches of rain a year, but most of it comes in two months. To keep plants and grass green it had to be irrigated the rest of the year. The roads and parking lot on the property were paved with asphalt to assure easy access during the rainy season and the few times there was a measurable snowfall. Culverts were installed under the road in several places to accommodate a fast runoff from the sloping terrain. Dr. Hare described the seasonal rains as "like a cow pissin' on a flat rock." One had to have been around cows to fully appreciate that description. He never failed to remind the ground crew to "check the culverts" before they left for the day. During a rain he could be seen in the middle of the night, dressed in yellow rain slicker and hat, black knee-high rubber boots, his location marked by the bobbing yellow beam of his flashlight as he went from culvert to culvert. He looked like a character out of a movie battling a "Noreaster." If tree limbs and debris were to collect in and stop the flow of water through the culvert, it would run over the top and wash out the asphalt road.

Chick Lanphier was made a member of the board of directors. His relationship with Hare had become more frequent, possibly because of the consulting contract which pertained to further developments of the sophisticated tape recorders in which Chick was personally interested. Probably it persisted more because they were on the same intellectual level. Both were accomplished mathematicians and creative. There the similarity ends. Chick came from wealth and was educated at Yale. He was recalcitrant as a teen-ager and flunked math until his father hired the high school math teacher to tutor him. Chick worked summers in the tool room and then full-time in his father's plant, eventually becoming president of the company, beating out his older brother who had been the heir apparent. During World War II Chick used his talents to advance the technology of Sonar. Dr. Hare, exposed to only a normal high school education learned his math as a consequence of his intellect and curiosity. Nothing was handed to him. Several times a year Chick made weekend visits to the Hare residence. The two men argued long into the night on a variety of subjects, most unrelated to business or engineering. Dr. Hare tried to convince Chick to temper his addiction to alcohol with no success. It was an adversarial friendship that endured until Chick Lanphier's death in 1978.

Business at the Grass Valley Group was slow and weeks passed without new orders. The Sangamo consulting contract helped. The State Department presented the company with a unique problem to solve. Many of the hotels in the Soviet Union had a telephone system that allowed them to monitor everything that was said in the room even if the telephone was not in use. Dr. Hare and Bill Rorden designed a device that could be placed over the telephone base. With the receiver in place the device generated noise so that any conversation taking place in the room could not be heard through the telephone receiver. If the hotel management came to the room to complain about noise in the telephone system, the diplomats knew someone tried to listen to their conversations. Associated with that gadget they used a Triplett volt meter, added a few components, and the end-product was an instrument the diplomat could use to check his room telephone line to see if it was bugged.

The A. B. Dick Company gave the GVG a contract to build a forerunner of what is known today as a fax machine. The ultimate customer was a railroad that wanted to accumulate waybill and manifest data during the day by optically scanning it on a revolving mirror system and recording it on tape. Then the data could be sent to several destinations over the telephone lines during the night at low rates. Using their knowledge of complex recording devices, Dr. Hare and Rorden made a dual speed machine that recorded data at a high speed, but because of so much interference on the telephone lines the data had to be sent at a slow speed to keep it readable. At the destination the data was received at the slow speed, reproduced at high speed, and printed. To record and play data at different speeds without distorting it was a unique problem. They delivered the working machine but believe it was never put into service.

Sangamo gave the company an order for a special recorder, but even with the consulting fee from Sangamo the company was experiencing hard financial times. Dr. Hare borrowed all he could on his life insurance policy, took out another loan using part of the Sangamo stock as collateral, and mortgaged the property. The Sangamo stock declined in price so the bank asked for payment or more collateral. Gradually Dr. Hare kept taking them more stock until they had all he owned. Soon the bank again threatened foreclosure.

Back in 1957, when he sold the Hare Company to Cinerama, Dr. Hare went to the Chase Manhattan Bank and purchased a cashier's check for $25,000. He carried that valuable piece of paper in his billfold for five years. It was security for a rainy day, like acorns buried by squirrels in the fall. All avenues had been used up. No more sources of credit were available. Now he knew the anguish his parents felt in the twenties when they watched their dreams evaporate. Dr. Hare and Hazel had a serious discussion. He took out the folded check, permanently creased and stained by the long confinement in the leather of his wallet.

"We can keep this and use it to start over somewhere, or we can put it in the company and it might last three months if we don't get a lot more business." He laid the check down on the dining table and straightened out its folds.

"Start where?" Hazel asked. "You don't like all the traveling with consulting and I can't see you as an employee working for a company."

"Then you think I should put this in the company?"

"It's up to you. But I don't think you have much choice."

Dr. Hare spent a restless night. Not for a second did he have a thought of applying for a government guaranteed loan. Never could he envision filling out the forms and explaining to some bureaucrat in Sacramento his plan of operation.

The next day the $25,000 discolored check was deposited in the bank. In the following weeks a few more orders came in for audio equipment, but not nearly enough to make current payments. Dr. Hare hadn't cashed his own paycheck for months. Again it looked like doomsday was approaching when Bill Rorden put in his savings of $20,000, which kept them alive a little longer. Several years had been lean for the young company, but 1962 was dismal. Too much late afternoon idle time was spent throwing darts at the target on the wall in the back of the machine shop. Dr. Hare injured a tendon in his knee being too competitive on his follow-through and was told by an orthopedic surgeon he had to wear soft shoes or face an operation that would probably leave him with a stiff knee. From then on he wore sneakers every day except on infrequent trips to San Francisco. That wasn't the only part of his wardrobe that changed when he moved to Grass Valley. He still wore the expensive Alpaca sweaters and the viyella shirts, but he changed the wool slacks to more practical chinos. Hazel had a problem. Dr. Hare was a man of unwavering habits and refused to change with the times. When he got dressed in the morning he put on his clothes in a certain sequence. Underwear, shirt, socks, shoes and then pants in that order. The current style of men's slacks had legs tapered narrow at the bottom. The pant legs were so narrow he could not put them on over his shoes, not even over the sneakers. Couldn't he vary his sequence and put his pants on before the shoes? Unthinkable. He had dressed this way for years. Hazel searched the stores, measuring cuff widths and trying to find unfashionable chinos with straight legs. She finally did. He wore sweaters and shirts from Abercrombie and Fitch, underwear and English wool socks from Brooks Brothers, and $12.95 chinos from Sears.

Business picked up slightly in 1963. More deliveries were made of the 610, 621, and 622 audio amplifiers to broadcast stations. Bob Johnson was hired as a technician and given his first assignment, winding transformers. Twenty-six-year-old Bob was no stranger to electronics. He spent four years in the Air Force as a radar technician and worked for an electronics company for a year before moving to Grass Valley. The second day on the job Dr. Hare stopped and watched him winding the transformers.

"You're too slow. You should be able to do that much faster," Dr. Hare said.

"Do you want quality or speed?" was the brash young man's reply. He immediately wished he had those words back.

"I want both," was the reply with the serious look and head nod with one eye half closed which most employees had seen at one time or another.

Bob survived the initial first few days and eventually became the most senior employee of the company in terms of years of service. He was included in the after-hours recreation in the plant with Dr. Hare and Stephen Hare.

Sometimes they set up a putting game with coffee cans placed around the factory and putted for money. Always any game had to include some small bets to satisfy the competitiveness of Dr. Hare. For variety there was indoor shooting with a pellet rifle at a target set up that trapped the pellets. The target was placed against a steel rolling door in the back wall of the plant. They became bored with the pellet gun so Dr. Hare brought out a .22 caliber target pistol and they fired it. The next morning the daylight streamed through a sieve-like pattern of holes in the steel door.

Bob was a good golfer. He hit a long ball and Dr. Hare liked to compete against him. Bob was always included in the Sunday foursome at Alta Sierra Country Club. Occasionally Dr. Hare would invite Bob to play on a week-day afternoon—just the two of them. This one time, which Bob will always remember, when the round was finished they went into the bar for the customary drink. After a bit of small talk about golf and past experiences, Bob mentioned the Grass Valley Group.

"Finish your drink. It's time to leave," Dr. Hare said abruptly to Bob.

On the trip back to the plant Dr. Hare was silent. The next morning he called Bob into his office and motioned to the couch. Bob knew then he was in for some "couch time" as it was called by the employees. He dreaded it.

Dr. Hare chewed him out and lectured for about an hour that business should never be discussed in public places where others could listen in. Social time was not for discussing business. He would not break his own rule so he said nothing on the way home and saved his reprimand for business hours the next day.

Audio equipment was so competitive the profit margins were very small, even for a low-overhead operation like the Grass Valley Group. The company manufactured almost everything in-house except for the electronic components. It manufactured its own metal cases, drilled printed circuit boards, even made shipping cartons from cardboard stock.

Quality and customer satisfaction were always emphasized to employees by Dr. Hare. He insisted that anyone testing circuits understand precisely the purpose of each component. When a piece of equipment was returned under warranty it was identified with a highly visible red tag. If Dr. Hare discovered a unit with a red tag not getting immediate attention, he demanded an explanation. Fast service on returned equipment was maintained even after the company started the policy of shipping a loaner immediately to the customer.

The beginning of 1963 the company was still looking for a proprietary product and barely able to pay its bills and make the payroll. Dr. Hare received a timely call from his former Stanford physics student, David Packard, that they might have a common interest and should have a talk. On the drive down to Palo Alto Dr. Hare and Hazel talked excitedly about the possibility of an association with the Hewlett-Packard organization. The success of his two former students, David Packard and Bill Hewlett, was well known to Dr. Hare and he was quite proud of them. To be affiliated with their company might be the catalyst the Grass Valley Group needed to get recognized and pointed in a new direction. As he got out of the car at the Stanford Industrial Park he had built himself up to expect a more optimistic scenario than he should have.

They greeted each other like old friends. Packard was a big athletic, man, with an outgoing personality. After the reminiscing they started talking business. Each was an experienced negotiator protecting his own interests. After two hours of discussions it was obvious that Packard expected much more than Dr. Hare was willing to give. Out of personal pride and as an experienced poker player, Dr. Hare did not hint at how badly he wanted some kind of arrangement that could rescue his company from its teetering financial condition. When Hazel drove up to get her husband she knew immediately he was disappointed and discouraged.

"Drive me to a liquor store. I need a drink," were his first words as he got in the car.

On the way he filled her in on the essential parts of the discussion that failed to culminate in any sort of an affiliation between the two companies. At the liquor store he purchased a pint of J & B.

"Take the Dumbarton Road bridge. It's a nice road."

It was the first time Hazel had ever driven in this area and after crossing the bridge she soon found the road was curving and narrow. Dr. Hare took a swig of the Scotch.

As it grew darker there were patches of fog, not a lot of traffic, but she was very tense.

"Isn't this a nice area," he repeated several times as he continued to sip the whiskey. The night became black and the asphalt absorbed the rays from the headlights. The curving narrow road and pockets of fog made it an exhausting drive. When they finally arrived at the Nut Tree Restaurant on the outskirts of Sacramento, the bottle of Scotch was empty and Dr. Hare was sound asleep. He didn't stir when she turned off the engine. Hazel left her spouse slumped in the car and went inside for a needed rest break and a cup of coffee. The gravity of the future financial condition of the company had not changed for the better and Hazel dreaded tomorrow.

AN OLD ACQUAINTANCE

During the small staff bull sessions talking about what the company should do to expand its products, the subject of television frequently came up. Dr. Hare thought of Harry Jacobs, who worked for him at the Airborne Instruments Laboratory during the war. He either knew or suspected Harry had returned to KGO in San Francisco so he decided to try to find him. Sure enough he was there.

"Donald Hare, Harry, here in Grass Valley."

"Well, Doc. What the hell are you doing in Grass Valley?"

"Started a little company making some recorders and audio equipment. But we need some business. Television keeps coming up so I thought I would pick your brains."

"That's a laugh. You picking my brains. I think there is a lot to be done in television. But you'll be up against some big ones. RCA, Ball Brothers, GE, Columbia. Tell you what, Doc. I'd like any excuse to come up to Grass Valley. I haven't been up that way for years. I'll bring a piece of

101

equipment and we can talk about what I think the industry needs."

"Great, Harry, we're out in the county on Bitney Spring Road."

That telephone call determined the destiny of the Grass Valley Group.

Harry Jacobs brought with him a distribution amplifier made by a company in the midwest. They took the cover off and examined its circuitry.

"Look at that, Bill. Not all that esoteric."

"Not a lot of hardware in there," Bill Rorden replied.

"What does this sell for, Harry?" Asked Dr. Hare.

"$350 and every TV station uses a lot of them."

"Wow, we've got to get in that business! The hell with audio," was Dr. Hare's reply.

They immediately started designing a distribution amplifier and with a few suggestions from Harry, adding some refinements the other manufacturers didn't offer. The audio business picked up. A big order came from a New York station and from another one in New Orleans. It was good business, just barely covering the overhead, but it brought in enough cash to keep the bank at bay.

Herby Hartman, chief engineer of Channel 3 in Sacramento, joined the Group in October of 1963. He, Bill Rorden and Dr. Hare put the finishing touches on the prototype of the 700 Distribution Amplifier. Stephen Hare, Dr. Hare's son, graduated with an EE degree from Stanford and started working for the group full time. Steve was tall and lanky, built similar to his father. He was a good athlete and, also like his father, a free thinker, which at times caused friction between the two. Most associates called him Corky after Corkhill, his second middle name, the same as his father's.

Herby Hartman took the new video model to New York in early 1964 and showed it to CBS and ABC. CBS didn't give it much of a look, but Hans Schmidt of ABC spent a week evaluating and analyzing the 700. After Hartman returned he and Rorden went to Chicago to the annual convention of the National Association of Broadcasters. The Grass Valley Group was not a member of the association. The company couldn't afford it. The two engineers set up the new equipment in their hotel room across the street from the Hilton where the convention was held. The pair hung around other equipment manufacturer's booths and talked to station engineers. Hartman knew some of them from having been in the industry for several years. They lured their prospects across the street to their hotel room for demonstrations. In a few months the company received orders for about fifty of the model 700 and a new modification designated as the 705.

The big break for the Grass Valley Group came in April.

Harry Jacobs was on the phone to Dr. Hare. "Doc, the American Broadcasting Company is going to broadcast the Republican National Convention from the Cow Palace in San Francisco." Harry's KGO was an ABC affiliate.

"We've just been told by our usual supplier it can't deliver the video equipment we need by May 1. If you can deliver by that date we'll give you an order for 10 Processing Amplifiers and 30 of your Distribution Amplifiers. I've seen your Distribution Amplifier, but not the Processing Amplifier."

"Sure we can do it. But what the hell is a Processing Amplifier?" Dr. Hare didn't even know there was such a device but agreed to build 10 of them.

Harry explained that all it had to do was clean up and restore the video signal to broadcast quality after its deterioration in wandering through monitors in various parts of the studio.

"Call Frank Haney in New York and he'll give you the specs," Harry added.

That was Monday. The wheels started turning. Tuesday afternoon Rorden and Dr. Hare went to town and bought a used television set to be used as a monitor so they could test what they were doing. A breadboard was put in a vise and they started soldering components into a newly designed circuit. On Wednesday Dr. Hare called Harry Jacobs.

"Come on up and see the Processing Amplifier working."

"Can't make it until Friday," was the reply.

"Fine. We'll have it in a case by then."

Harry Jacobs came up Friday, saw the new video equipment working and called New York. "They did it! Give them an order!"

The equipment was delivered to San Francisco on time and worked perfectly during the broadcast of the convention. ABC became the most important customer of the Group. That saved the year 1964 and set the momentum for 1965, which would be the first really profitable year for the young company.

The increased activity at the Grass Valley Group created more local notice and gossip and enhanced the reputation of the mysterious and reclusive eccentric Dr. Hare. Most were unfounded and stretched well beyond factual incidents. He was not widely known as a soft touch for causes, such as his annual contribution to a young 4H girl who was raising a farm animal. Dr. Hare didn't want it known publicly and was embarrassed when they brought him a plaque in recognition of his gift. His favorite television program was "Family Affair" with Brian Keith and Sebastian Cabot, and he was intrigued with "The Rockford Files" starring his favorite actor, Jim Garner. The advances in electronic organs tantalized his musical talents. He purchased a chord organ, bought some sheet music and taught himself to play it.

Two new video models were developed in 1965, the Synac and Sync Generator. The company had no sales department, did no advertising, but word spread through the industry about its quality equipment. To introduce the new products to the industry the Grass Valley Group joined the NAB and leased a modest little display booth in a low traffic area for the 1965 convention. It was one of the lower priced locations, away from the splendor and hype associated with the large companies. Nevertheless, it attracted enough attention that orders started coming in during the following months.

This was at a time when the television broadcast industry was expanding rapidly. Additional channels were added, new stations started up and money was to be made. The established equipment companies had the inside track because they had a complete line. RCA sold a complete station. It installed the transmitter, cameras, monitors, amplifiers, both video and audio and arranged for financing. But it also developed new equipment slowly because it took a long time for an idea to go through its bureaucracy of engineering, drafting, tool design, testing, and writing of manuals.

GVG had no drafting department and tools were made from hands-on need, not from blueprints. When a new idea took shape Dr. Hare and Rorden did not study it to death. After a few hours of discussion the two engineers put breadboards in place and started soldering. They searched through the catalogs of solid state components and built a prototype in a matter of days, or at most in a few weeks. One of the secrets of the reliability of the GVG equipment was its choice of components. The main frame computer industry became the largest user of transistors as they replaced vacuum tubes. Those used in computers were being manufactured by the millions. The more they made the more reliable they became. When Dr. Hare approached a design challenge he tried to use transistors that were used in computers, because of their reliability. He tended to stay away from new ones made for special applications and in limited quantities. It was not unusual for him to spend hours searching through the transistor reference books and then calling the manufacturer for "engineering samples."

He had a work bay just outside his office, two benches placed in an "L" almost covered with components, a wheel of resistors, soldering iron, snips, oscilloscope, and testing equipment that ran continuously. A breadboard, a circuit board on which components are soldered to create a new circuit, was always in its special vise. Against the wall stood a row of metal shelves loaded with small sacks and boxes of the transistor engineering samples. Bill Rorden had an identical work area adjacent to Dr. Hare's.

On Dr. Hare's cluttered work benches there was one clear space. It was for the "puppies," Itsy and Red. Actually they were full grown Dachshunds but he had gotten them as puppies and still called them such. Almost every morning he brought them to the plant. Dr. Hare picked them up and put them in their spot next to a heat lamp and they slept for a while as he worked. If he walked away for a time and they wanted down, the puppies barked for help. Dr. Hare had trained them never to jump off the bench for fear they would injure their backs. They had special treatment and were the reason for the strict five-miles-an-hour speed limit on the property.

Dr. Hare and "Red."

109

Dr. Hare's choice of the transistors he put in his circuits was just one of the reasons for the reliability of the components of the Grass Valley Group's equipment. Careful testing and "burn-in" time before shipment assured reliability which was as important, or perhaps more important, as innovation. Down time meant a loss of revenue or source of embarrassment for the television stations and networks. GVG guaranteed its product would perform at the original specifications for two years or it would be replaced immediately at no charge. One engineer at a television station said, "When I take a piece of Grass Valley equipment out of the box and plug it in I know it will work." To reduce exposure to rough handling in transit, all equipment was shipped only by air in double strength oyster-colored cartons. Should a piece of equipment fail for any reason, which was seldom, a replacement was shipped by air to the customer the same day.

One incident that didn't hurt the GVG reputation happened at a golf tournament when a television equipment truck was struck by lightning and everything was damaged. Clearly this was not covered by the warranty but GVG replaced it all, at no charge. Bill Rorden said lightning struck twice when he had to rush to get the replacements in production.

With the exception of its first video equipment, the distribution amplifier, the company never designed and manufactured a piece of equipment just to take business from another company. Most of its models, and soon there were a total of 70, were designed from the needs expressed by the engineers in the television network engineers at San Francisco and Los Angeles. It was a fast-growing business with new problems and new ideas calling for new solutions. The quick response from ideas to solutions by Rorden and Dr. Hare gave them the edge over the competition.

Although GVG prices were competitive, and most of the time below similar models of other companies, Dr. Hare felt the company had been charging too much for the sync generator. He informed all purchasers of that model they would receive a retroactive credit up to $500. GVG's pricing formula was very simple. They looked at the pieces of hardware in it and applied a multiple that seemed fair. If it was in the area of what the industry would pay, they made it and sold it. If it was going to cost too much they didn't make it.

The first few months of 1966 indicated it would be the best year ever. Orders were coming in faster than they could be filled. For the first time the company had a sizable backlog. Bob Johnson, Stephen Hare, Bill Rorden and Dr. Hare were working every Saturday to try to keep up. There were temporary distractions caused by the shop's television set when 7-foot 2-inch Lew Alcindor was playing for UCLA. Hazel Hare made almost daily trips to the Sacramento airport in a small station wagon filled with boxes of equipment. As business improved the task was taken over by a full-time driver and a van.

With the new-found prosperity the landscaping was completed. Joe Ruess, an area landscaper and nursery owner, made regular trips planting willows, magnolias, poplars, mountain ash and pampas grass creating a park-like area around the plant. Iris and daffodils were naturalized in spots around the trees. In a few years every Spring the sloping grassy area facing the entrance to the property erupted into a golden quilt and was given the title of "Daffodil Hill" by the employees. Picnic tables were placed where employees ate lunch in the tranquil environment. Litter was not a problem. Employees were very considerate of the natural surroundings.

A perk that all employees enjoyed during the long growing season was the company garden. An area on one side of the property was plowed and made into a vegetable and fruit garden enclosed with a 10-foot-high deer fence. There were peach, apple, apricot and Black Mission fig trees. The latter was Dr. Hare's favorite. Two kinds of grape vines bordered the plot, possibly because of a childhood recollection of his father's vineyards. In the spring it was planted with corn, green onions, carrots, tomatoes, peppers and summer squash. During the harvest season every afternoon the maintenance crew would bring flats of fresh-picked vegetables and fruit for employees to take home.

After the Grass Valley Group finished the special recorder for Sangamo and the consulting contract ended, Chick and Dr. Hare talked occasionally, with Chick being brought up to date on what was going on in the company. Chick knew the business was growing and Dr. Hare needed someone in the administration area. Chick recommended me. I was in the financial area of Sangamo and wanted to make a climate change because of recurring asthma. Dr. Hare hired me as controller, later to be secretary and treasurer of the company. During our interview I said I was not versed in corporate income tax regulations.

"Don't worry about it. There's the complete set of the Commerce Clearing House Income Tax Regulations," he said, and pointed to the bookcase. "I've read every volume. You can read them anytime you want."

On the first day I reported to work wearing jacket and tie. "We're casual here. No jacket and tie," said Dr. Hare. I knew he was going to tell me that, but wanted to hear it from him.

Dr. Hare always wanted to know exactly what was going on in all departments of the company. Every day the bookkeeper kept a continuous daily table with three numbers: the cash receipts, disbursements and bank balance. And every day Dr. Hare looked at it and checked the addition and subtraction. If an error was detected he issued a sharp reprimand. He also had a few strict rules. Employees were instructed to never lay a receiver down without putting the telephone on hold. "O. K." should be eliminated from one's vocabulary during telephone conversations with customers.

Dr. Hare was enough of an environmentalist that he hated to see any form of animal or plant life taken. He did allow spraying for earwigs when they invaded the desks. Office girls screamed when they opened drawers alive with the one-inch beetle-like insects with waving antenna. Mouse traps had to be kept out of Dr. Hare's sight under the metal stock shelves. When one of the little critters was caught the trap had to be emptied before he came into the plant in the morning. There were plenty of rattlesnakes in the upper elevation of the property as evidenced by the discarded white translucent skins on the ground. But no effort was made to eliminate them unless one strayed near his residence, even though once he had lost a dog to a rattlesnake. It was Shadrack, a champion Red Cocker Spaniel he had brought from Connecticut. The dog had been missing and when they finally found him he was lying in the entrance to an abandoned mine, dying from a snake bite. When Dr. Hare walked the wilderness area, which he did often, he carried a golf club, tapping it on the ground to allow any nearby snake to retreat under the Manzanita bushes. A small herd of deer trailed through the property every evening and a few Mallard ducks made their home on the little lake. Lizards were numerous and were often seen doing pushups on the rocks.

Suddenly late one afternoon it was discovered there was no water at the plant or Dr. Hare's residence. A check of the water tank confirmed it was empty. Dr. Hare and I each took a walkie talkie and started walking the line where the plastic water pipe was buried from the tank down to the spring, hoping to step on a squishy spot. It was five o'clock and the maintenance people had gone home. When the break was located we got a couple of shovels and started digging a muddy hole, Dr. Hare on one side, myself on the other. After twenty minutes or so of digging I said, "This is a helluva job for the treasurer of the company."

Dr. Hare replied, "If you want to come around and dig from this side you can be president."

No question about it, Dr. Hare loved this property. The sound of aircraft dropping slurry on a forest fire miles away made him nervous. "If we should have a fire and lose these trees I would have to leave. I couldn't stand to live with the desolation."

The cleared area around the plant and lake were irrigated constantly in the dry season to keep it green, not only for looks, but to reduce the fire hazard. A gasoline engine-driven portable pump with fire hose was placed beside the lake. A second reservoir was built half-way up the hill and water piped to it for a second source of water for fire fighting. Much of the brush on the property was Manzanita, especially thick on the upper level. When this bush is ignited it burns very hot and is difficult to extinguish. The maintenance crew spent part of their daily schedule clearing fire lanes through the brush to retard the spreading of any fire that might be started by accident or lightning.

Frequent thunderstorms in the summer months or a wet snow in late winter occasionally caused tree limbs to fall on power lines interrupting electric service to the plant. Once a car hit a power pole on Highway 20 that put the plant down for a day. The increase in sales resulted in a substantial backlog that made it essential to have a backup source of power to avoid a loss of production. A Kohler generator was installed with an automatic switcher. When the voltage dropped from the utility, the generator automatically started. Every Monday morning the switch was thrown and the plant operated a few minutes on the standby generator to be sure it was operative if and when a power failure occurred.

The additional new volume of business made it necessary to increase the circuit board assembly area. More women were added to stuff the boards with components. The final assembly area was crowded and the metal shop needed more space.

Dr. Hare left his shop bay and motioned to me.

"Let's take a walk." That was not too unusual, we did that often. But this was not an inspection tour. We walked for an hour, stopping and looking at the terrain, the slope, and most importantly, the trees. We were looking for a site to place an additional building for expanding production facilities. No area appeared to be satisfactory. To level another building site would disturb too much of the natural beauty or call for removing too many trees. The latter was unthinkable. We walked over to the fence along the adjacent ranch. Cows were grazing in a cleared area bordered by towering pines.

"Talk to the Kohlers. They have about forty acres. Bill lives there alone and his sister works in town. At the lumber yard, I think," Dr. Hare said to me. "First see if you can get an option, say for up to one year. We may want it sooner."

The Kohler ranch was an ideal property since it had several cleared areas and no expensive improvements. I had several discussions with both of the Kohlers and they were willing to grant an option to the company for the purchase of their property.

"There's one drawback," I told Dr. Hare, "The owners of the property above have legal access through the Kohler ranch. That's the only way they can get to it."

"I think I knew that," replied Dr. Hare. "He's the bastard I talked to when I heard he was going to sell all the timber on that property he inherited, just to pay the taxes. I tried to get him to hold off and he got nasty. Told me he also owned the mineral rights under this property. Burns me every time I think about it."

I called Frank Francis, the company's local attorney. "Frank, get the description of the Kohler ranch and draft an option for us to buy it. I've talked to them and it looks favorable. Try not to attract any attention. I don't want any competition."

Within a week the price was agreed to and the option signed, making room for expansion. The company's products were being accepted by more of the industry. New television stations were specifying certain models of Grass Valley Group equipment in their orders to the larger manufacturers. It was not unusual for a station signing a big contract with RCA for transmitter, cameras and other station equipment to include several GVG models.

A lady and her four sons visited the plant on a Sunday morning. She owned the television station in Thermopolis, Idaho. It was run by the four boys.

"Do you mean I can replace that whole room full of equipment I have with just that one rack?" she exclaimed as Stephen Hare was showing her the GVG models and explaining their technical advantages to the sons. They became customers and were on the phone often to Stephen.

Business was good enough that Dr. Hare made it policy that the company would not take any government contracts. One day a purchasing agent of the State Department called and said they were interested in talking about ordering an additional quantity of the telephone devices the company manufactured for them a few years before.

"I have no knowledge that equipment has been declassified therefore I will not discuss it on the telephone," was his immediate response that ended the conversation. After he hung up, he said, "We took that too cheap and we don't have time for it."

Occasionally the company received government bid requests for electronic equipment. Bill Rorden studied the specifications and if one of the company's standard models fit the specifications, he would submit a bid at the regular retail price. Anything else would be tossed in the waste basket.

One day a telegram was received from NASA asking if the company wanted to correct the bid on a certain item. Bill took a look at a copy of the proposal and said, "Tell 'em no." He didn't waste words. When NASA received the answer to the telegram its purchasing agent telephoned and the call was given to me.

"We think you have made a mistake. Your bid is $2,000 less than the next lowest bid and if you have made a mistake we feel obligated to let you correct it." NASA's procurement agent explained.

"We appreciate your consideration. But that piece of equipment is a standard production model of ours and the price we quoted you is the same price we charge television stations and networks all over the country. If you want it at that price you can have it."

That was the beginning of a good relationship with NASA as they purchased several pieces of GVG production models. Later some of its offers for bids read, "equivalent to Grass Valley Group Model No..."

Even better than we had hoped, 1966 was shaping up to be a good year. Sales were over twice that of 1965; net profit increased five fold; the company net worth tripled. Cash flow was adequate to cover the increase in business, but to be prepared for building expansion a loan agreement was made with the Mother Lode Bank. In October I was made a corporate director and at the November Board of Directors meeting was elected treasurer and secretary.

In December I was offered the privilege of buying five percent of the corporate stock which was closely held by Dr. Hare, Hazel Hare, Stephen Hare and Bill Rorden.

Further expansion was mandatory or the company would stand to lose business with unrealistic extended delivery dates. The purchase of the adjacent Kohler ranch was closed. To save time the company decided to build a second building identical to the first one rather than experience a delay drawing up new plans. Dr. Hare and I walked over the new property and settled on a site that had no large trees, except for one that would be spared by cutting a hole in the overhanging roof. To access the new building a winding road was laid out between the trees. Dr. Hare hated to lose a tree and so often when one was injured the Pine Beetles entered the wound and eventually killed the tree. The large Ponderosa pines next to the new road had their trunks covered with two-by-four lumber to protect them from accidental scarring by the heavy earth-moving equipment. The machine operators expressed their displeasure at this measure as they considered it a lack of confidence in their skills. The two-by-fours took a few hits. The contractors were hired, the site was leveled, and another redwood water tank was erected to supply the new building.

After the small reservoir described earlier was finished, electric power was run up to it so a pump could be installed for fire protection. A stake was driven in the ground to show the utility where to set the pole and switch box. For some reason they put it about 20 feet north of the stake. I wondered why. On the wall in Dr. Hare's office was an aerial photograph of the property taken a few months before. It showed clearly the fences along the property which were assumed to be the property lines. The angle of the fence line made me suspicious that the power company perhaps knew something about the boundary lines that no one in the company knew. I called the maintenance supervisor and asked him come to the reservoir and bring a machete. After fifteen or twenty minutes of hacking weeds we found what we were looking for, a brass marker.

I returned to Dr. Hare's office. "It looks like we just built a reservoir on the neighbor's property."

"How the hell did you discover that?"

I gave him the details. This was the neighbor with whom Dr. Hare had unfriendly words over the harvesting of the timber. "If he wants to cause any trouble we can give him the reservoir and if wants to sue, you should know he cut down two big trees on our property."

The company was now on a building binge which continued for several years. A small guest house was built on the highest point of the property for the convenience of V. I. P. visitors. For security and utility it was deemed advisable to have the maintenance supervisor live on the property, so a house was built for him and his family.

With the large cash expenditures going into the construction it was time to borrow some funds from the Mother Lode Bank. I called Coy Miller, the bank manager, and told him the company wanted to utilize the loan agreement, the amount it wanted to borrow and made an appointment. When I arrived at the bank the note was ready and Miller handed it to me to sign. The amount and interest rate and length of time in the body of the note was according to what was agreed. But there was a rubber stamp overprint that stated the loan could be called at any time prior to the due date.

"What's the idea of this rubber stamp, Coy?" I asked.

"Oh, that's just routine. We do it all the time. Doesn't mean a thing. We would never call the loan on you."

"I'm glad to hear you say that. Since it doesn't mean a thing you won't mind doing it over and leave that off."

"Oh, no. I can't do that. I assure we would never exercise the call."

"Coy, and I assure you that if I signed that note, next week I wouldn't be treasurer of the Grass Valley Group. Maybe you would rather hear from Dr. Hare."

"I gotta talk to our attorney. I'll call you after lunch."

Coy called and said they had prepared a new note with no call provision.

The operating style of Dr. Hare was not typical of corporate chief operating officers. He encouraged expressions of individual opinions even if they were opposite to his. In one meeting when everyone was silent except him he was perturbed. "I want your opinion. Dammit, I'm paying you guys too much to just sit there and agree with me." And he meant it. More than once when he and Bill Rorden were discussing how to handle the logic of a complicated circuit, he would take what he knew was the wrong approach just to draw Rorden out to defend the other way. It was his way of making sure they were exploring all avenues of the logic.

Dr. Hare called a meeting of Rorden, Stephen Hare, Hazel Hare and me, specifically to talk about how the company needed to grow to include services now performed by outside companies, and to expand the product line by acquiring small companies.

"Like it or not, we're still in the audio business and we can't continue to discourage orders for it," Dr. Hare said. "Let's see if we can find a company which already has a name in the business. In the other technical areas, I've talked to Chick Lanphier and if he runs across any likely candidates he'll let us know."

Rorden made a motion that Dr. Hare and I be authorized to look for companies to acquire.

"One more thing," Dr. Hare added. "Bill and I have decided to re-design almost every model we have. It will be called the 900 series and incorporate new features we think the industry will want. It's a gamble. Unless it's well accepted it could just hurt the sales of the 700 series and not develop any new business."

An engineer from RCA called Dr. Hare and said they wanted a license to manufacture one of the GVG models. "We don't license any of our products." Dr. Hare replied, "It's a waste of time. The industry is changing too fast. Right now we are re-designing every piece of equipment in our line. In another 30 days that model will be obsolete. Go ahead and copy it, we don't care. This is where we have the advantage. We see a need for a piece of equipment and make it. Sometimes in ten days. You have to get committee approval, design the circuit, send it to drafting, give the parts a lot of numbers, make requisitions to purchasing and it's two years before you can get anything into production. Yeah, go ahead and copy it." He really enjoyed that conversation.

The first candidate for acquisition was Ron Schwartzman, owner of a small shop called Graphics-Silkscreen, located on the outskirts of Sacramento. He had been doing excellent work for the company on panels and circuit boards for several years. Just he and his wife worked in the business they started with almost no capital. Schwartzman had expressed his desire to expand more into graphics arts so he seemed to be an ideal candidate to become a part of the Grass Valley Group. The company offered to set him up as president of a new corporation called Technical Arts, Inc. He would own 20 percent, the Grass Valley Group 80 percent. Immediately, $5,000 in working capital would be put into the company with an additional $10,000 to purchase new equipment including facilities for etching circuit boards. His starting salary was agreed upon and the company formed the new corporation. At the last minute he backed out.

Stephen Hare and I went to Sacramento to talk acquisition to a manufacturer of audio equipment well established in the radio station market. The conversation didn't last long since the week before the owner had signed an agreement to be acquired by another company.

When we returned I reported to Dr. Hare that there was no possibilty of a deal. "Besides, you wouldn't have gotten along with him."

"What makes you say that?"

"It's just a feeling I had. He seemed to be superficial. And you don't like that type. He had an empty Lancers ceramic wine bottle on his bookshelf."

"A Lancers wine bottle? He saved a Lancers wine bottle?" Dr. Hare shook his head.

Dr. Hare had known Si Krinsky for years. Si was a manufacturer's representative selling mostly audio equipment. One company he represented was Alma Radio in San Diego and he told Dr. Hare they might be a good prospect for an acquisition. They made a good product but were having financial problems. In fact, Si was loaning the owner money to meet his payroll, trying to keep him in business.

Bill Rorden, Stephen Hare and I flew to San Diego to talk to Alma Radio, named after the owner's mother-in-law. It was a small operation with a modest amount of equipment and low overhead. Rorden looked at the circuits and pointed out how a few minor changes of the solid state components could improve the design. He seemed interested and agreed to come up to Grass Valley to talk about the possibility of being a part of the Group. A couple of weeks went by with no word from Alma Radio. Si called and asked what was going on.

"He seems interested and said he is going to come up and talk to Dr. Hare, but we haven't heard from him," I told Si.

"I want to keep him in business. I loaned him some more money to meet his payroll."

"You aren't helping us by loaning him money. Cut it out, Si, and maybe he'll be more anxious to talk."

The owner finally came up and met with Dr. Hare, who explained that he wanted Alma Radio to operate much the same and that GVG would furnish working capital and engineering help. An agreement on price was reached, sealed with a handshake until it could be finalized with a written agreement. It had one unique feature. If Alma operated for the first year at a profit, an additional $25,000 would be added to the price. After the owner returned to San Diego and thought it over, he backed out.

Finding a company suitable for acquisition was difficult enough, but consummating a takeover was even more elusive. One attempt that never got off the ground was interest in a small company in Indiana called Texscan. Chick Lanphier knew of it and GVG had one of its test instruments. Apparently they had some very good engineering talent, but Chick indicated they were not well financed. GVG had a brokerage account with Francis I. DuPont in Sacramento, which was asked if its Indianapolis office could find out more about the company. Instead, the Sacramento broker called the company and told them GVG was interested, possibly to buy it. When that was reported to Dr. Hare a "WHAT!" erupted like it came from a bullhorn. He called the manager of Francis I. Dupont who defended the actions of the broker. The next day the account was closed and moved to Merrill Lynch.

In April 1967 Dr. Hare returned from the NAB Convention convinced the company had to expand production because of the good reception of the new equipment models. It was the first time GVG had a professionally designed, but modest, display booth. He called Bill Rorden, Stephen Hare and me into his office.

"We have a serious problem. If we let our backlog get beyond 12 weeks we're in deep trouble. When the response we received at the convention turns into orders in the next few months we have to be ready for it. If we can't deliver in a reasonable time and the word gets around we're going to lose business," Dr. Hare emphasized with his familiar nod and wink.

It was still a small company. A production manager was hired and the circuit board stuffing department enlarged again. All this without a sales department.

Possibly as a result of the Grass Valley Group's presence at the NAB Convention, another merger option appeared. William C. Kuhns of Fenton and Company and Don Clark of Continental Electronics proposed the acquisition of the "Prolog" equipment line and a possible merger with a company called Controlled Circuits.

The "Prolog" equipment was an automatic programming system for AM and FM radio stations. Clark furnished information on sales forecast, inventory details, estimated cost of manufacturing the units, pricing and the competitive position of the product. Kuhns proposed several options on financing the purchase of the line, the merger of the companies and the percentages of ownership. GVG would manufacture the units and some of the technical people would probably come with the product line. Dr. Hare sought advice from his old friend Hazard Reeves several times. Reeves knew all aspects of the radio business.

When Rorden and Dr. Hare received the technical data on the equipment, the list of bought outside parts and assemblies, they came to the conclusion the product had a much too low gross margin. In-house manufacturing of some of the purchased parts would not reduce costs substantially. No matter what kind of a financial deal Kuhns could put together, the product had to be produced at a profit and Dr. Hare was skeptical. While he wanted to expand, someone else's white elephant was not the way to go. Another merger attempt came to naught.

At the board of directors meeting on the 16th of January, I reported on my recent trip to Palo Alto to Pacific Communications and Electronics which was interested in merger talks with GVG. I spent most of the time with its vice-president and learned details of its operation, products and work history of the key people in the organization. Several of its people were invited up to Grass Valley for further talks. Again nothing developed from this effort.

A SURPRISE DECISION

A group of settler emigrants coming west through Truckee in 1849 camped near the junction of Steep Hollow and Bear River. Their cattle wandered off and were found grazing on the lush grass in a meadow which they named Grass Valley. Fifty miles south the discovery of gold at Sutter's Mill received all the excitement and a place in the history books. But a year later an outcropping of gold in quartz rock was the second largest discovery in California's history. Half the gold mined in the state came from the mines around Grass Valley. That era ended in 1956 when the last of the mine machinery was auctioned off. All of the gold was not necessarily buried in the hills as Dr. Hare brought new technology to the region in the use of gold-plated circuit boards and electronic connectors. The early days were similar to a hard-rock miner's hardship. A find and then the vein ran out. Going from gloom to hope and determination, Dr. Hare and Bill Rorden finally discovered a rich vein, a place in the mother lode of the rich and exciting domain of television. They staked out their claim armed with expertise, creativity and imagination. The result was a growing business never seen in the area since the closing of the mines.

They were not modest. "We can build anything," Dr. Hare exclaimed. "We discovered there was more ignorance in the video equipment business than in audio and proceeded to take advantage of it," Bill Rorden said.

The company was prospering and growing. The formula for growth was creating new products, not just manufacturing to compete. Now it could afford CONRAC monitors, the standard in the industry, instead of retail television sets. A few luxuries were added to the property. Several grassy areas around the lake were mowed close to resemble golf greens and a small putting green was built just outside the front door. Sometimes during lunch break the usual Sunday foursome would chip and putt for dimes, and after the workers went home golf balls would be hit over the empty parking lot to several areas of the property. Used golf balls were purchased by the gunny sack from a man in Ohio and cleaned in Mrs. Hare's washing machine until it broke. The tees were improved, and several sizes of gravel and sand were hauled in for the base for a couple of new greens to be built in a professional way.

For at least five years Dr. and Mrs. Hare had not taken a vacation trip. In fact, Dr. Hare was almost a recluse on "the reservation." He left the confines of the property only to get a haircut, which he seldom needed because of creeping baldness, or go to the dentist, and the Sunday golf game at Alta Sierra Country Club with Stephen, Bob Johnson and me. He liked golf and could still break eighty when he was in his middle sixties. He understood the game, and as

a teen-ager was a contender in the California State Junior championship.

One day Dr. Hare announced he and Hazel were going on vacation, a drive up through the northwest. The timing was coincidental, but while the Hares were gone I ordered a big semi-flatbed-truckload of bent grass sod for the greens and blue grass for the tees. It came from Cal Turf near Sacramento and took all day for its crew and the company maintenance workers to install. White sand for a bunker was going to be hauled up from Carmel but that was ruled out as too extravagant.

Then came the big surprise. Dr. Hare called me from Orcas Island.

"I've been thinking it over and Hazel and I have talked about it. We have decided to take the company public!"

There was stunned silence.

"Did you hear me?"

"Yes, I heard you. You want to take the company public. I was surprised."

"We've given it a lot of thought. We'll be back the end of next week. You get things started. You know some people. Make some appointments."

"Yes, sir," was all I could think of.

I hung up, still finding it hard to believe what I had heard.

"Stephen, come here a minute!" I yelled out the door to the shop.

"What's up?"

"I just talked to your Dad. He's at Orcas Island. He said he wants to take the company public."

"Can't believe it. He won't stand for people looking over his shoulder. Naw, he'll change his mind."

"I couldn't believe it either. But he asked me to start making appointments with brokers."

For months Dr. Hare had been concerned about a problem that a few years ago he never dreamed he would ever have. The company was growing fast and making a healthy profit. Above average profits were the result of keeping the overhead low, like no sales expense, and modest salaries to the officers. The profits were necessary for working capital to sustain the growth, add new buildings and equipment with minimal borrowing. The corporation had paid income tax once on the profits, but by keeping in the business the remainder of the profits the Retained Earnings account on the balance sheet was growing each year. The IRS could determine the retained earnings were excessive for the size of the company and assess an additional tax even though the earnings had already been taxed once. Dr. Hare thought this was confiscatory and penalized growing small businesses. For months he stewed over this problem and decided the only way to avoid this unfair tax was to increase the capitalization of the company. This was a significant factor in his decision to take the company public.

The next day I called John Markham at Hornblower and Weeks in Chicago. When I was with Sangamo I had known John and his father. The senior Markham was a director of Sangamo, had his own investment company for years and had merged into Hornblower and Weeks. I briefly told John about the progress of the company and the decision to take it public. I asked him to send someone from their San Francisco office to come up and talk to Dr. Hare when he returned.

The next week the manager of the San Francisco office of Hornblower and Weeks drove up to Grass Valley and spent several hours looking at the facilities, the financial numbers and explaining what was involved in bringing out an initial public stock offering. At lunch we went up to the Hares' residence. For me it was always a treat to have lunch there as Hazel Hare often fixed a cheese soufflé that was out of this world. That and a tossed salad and ice tea made a perfect lunch. Their long dining table was of solid black walnut hand-crafted by a skillful Italian cabinet maker who hand-rubbed it with many coats of oil. It was always a topic of conversation for any new guest.

The gentleman was very informative as to all the steps necessary to get ready for a public issue, but he did not recommend that his firm handle it.

"We can if you insist, and I know you are acquainted with John Markham, but we don't do a very good job on small issues. And I don't know why, but we don't. We had one a short time ago and it just didn't work out. It's not just bringing out the issue, but it's service to the market afterwards. I recommend you ask John for some underwriters who are better suited for a small issue."

It was a disappointment but it was good advice and we had a better picture of the road ahead. Our secretary knew a broker in San Francisco, Irving Lundborg Company, so I called that firm and mailed financial statements with a brief history of the Grass Valley Group. In the following week I had several telephone conversations with Bernard Fesbach and John J. Gardiner, Jr. on taking the company public.

"Mr. Fesbach is on the phone for you," came the secretary's voice from the outer office.

"Good morning, Mr. Fesbach."

"We've gone over the information you gave us. The numbers are very impressive. John and I would like to come up and discuss a few things with you. How about next Wednesday, July 19?"

"Just a minute while I check Dr. Hare's calendar." I put the phone on hold and asked Dr. Hare if Wednesday would be allright. It was like playing office because we both knew he would be available.

"Wednesday is clear."

"Fine, we should be there about nine o'clock."

"We'll be expecting you."

Nine o'clock! That meant they had to leave the city before five, but not unusual for stockbrokers on the Pacific coast to be up that early since they have to be in the office when the exchange opens in New York four hours earlier.

They arrived on schedule, two impeccably groomed men in dark suits with slim ties hanging loose down the front of white shirts. They contrasted starkly the natural environment of pines, mountain ash, rocks and grass surrounding the small lake. I greeted them followed by the customary handshakes and introductions.

"Dr. Hare will be down in a few minutes. I'll show you around the plant," I said, and led the way into the final assembly and testing area. Then we walked over to building No.2 to the metal shop, plating room and the production area where the women were stuffing circuit boards with capacitors and resistors.

Back to the main building we walked into office area. Dr. Hare was at his desk.

"Dr. Hare this is Bernard Feshbach, John Gardiner."

Dr. Hare dropped his pencil on the yellow legal pad in front of him on the table, unwound his lean frame from his oak swivel chair, stood up and stuck out his hand for a brief soft handshake. His was neither limp nor a bone crusher. His gaze was almost a stare, one of sizing up and unrevealing.

"Did Bob show you around the facility?"

"Oh, yes. We were impressed. Such beautiful surroundings," offered Feshbach. They were motioned to have a seat on the sofa facing Dr. Hare's table.

"We like it. I think our employees appreciate the natural beauty around them rather than a stark industrial park."

Again a contrast. Dr. Hare in his chinos, long arms hanging out of a colorful short-sleeved sport shirt, white Sperry canvas "topsiders" and sagging black socks. Me in a white, short-sleeved shirt left over from my former corporate employment, and no tie. The gentlemen kept their broker costumes intact, never shedding their jackets.

After a few minutes of small talk about San Francisco's Montgomery Street and a restaurant where one can get fresh-squeezed orange juice, Dr. Hare got to the business.

"We have been successful in designing products for the television broadcasting industry and manufacturing them to sell at competitive prices and make a very satisfactory profit. Damn satisfactory. I'll bet you can't name another company that makes 21 percent net profit after taxes." He raised his head with a smile and then continued. "We have no salesmen, don't advertise. Everything is word of mouth and although we have stepped up production our backlog is at times uncomfortably long. We want to expand into more phases of the industry, new products, and educational TV—"

Feshbach interrupted. Dr. Hare stopped and stared. He didn't like being interrupted when he was making a point.

"Rather than going public with an initial public offering, there are other avenues that might well serve your purpose. Institutional financing using a loan agreement backed by equity conversion privileges."

Gardiner inserted, "There are several groups of venture capital investors in the Bay Area who could be contacted."

"And there is always a possibility of a merger with a larger company," Feshbach resumed.

I observed Dr. Hare. "These guys are shooting themselves in the foot," I thought. "They think they are dealing with a scientist who is lost in his own little world of slide rules. They don't know he has started and sold more than one company, reads the Wall Street Journal and has read the full set of Commerce Clearing House income tax regulations. They will not be asked to stay for lunch."

Dr. Hare made little effort to hide his exasperation. "Gentlemen, we had you come here to discuss the possibility of the company going public. I am well aware of all the alternatives you have thrown out and none are appropriate. I don't want to discuss them."

He continued, "You have seen our numbers and I don't think I'm being immodest to say the profits we are making are pretty damn impressive." He waited for a response.

"When we plan an issue a 12 to 15 PE ratio is as high as we feel is marketable. Really, we prefer 12," Gardiner said. Feshbach nodded.

"When you look at our record and that of similar offerings I don't see why the ratio can't be higher," Dr. Hare replied.

"There's the after-market, keeping happy shareholders, the corporate image. And the reputation of Irving Lundborg Co."

"In other words, you wouldn't bring out an issue at what you thought was too high a price as it might have a deleterious effect on your reputation?"

"Well, we would like to have you aware of all the ramifications," Gardiner hedged.

"Let's take an example," Dr. Hare said. "Riker Video Industries, Inc. went public a year ago. It is similar to GVG in size, sales, net worth. It's in the same market but we compete on only one piece of equipment. Their profit is very modest compared to ours. It was brought out at 7 1/2 by a firm called Michael G. Kletz & Associates. Ever hear of them?"

Dr. Hare had done his homework.

"No, and I must emphasize the importance of dealing with a well-known and reputable company like Irving Lumborg. Especially important in the after-market," Feshbach repeated again.

"Let's see what the stock is doing now a year later," Feshbach said as he stood up and went for the phone to call his office, confident he was going to score a point.

Riker traded that day at 43.

"Wish I hadn't called." The broker was deflated.

That ended the discussion for the day.

Later that evening, Fesbach called me at home and said that on the trip back to the city he re-thought the ratios and if we wanted to go at 20 times the profit we could get it. Then he went into a lecture about responsibility of the corporation to its employees and shareholders.

On the morning of July 20, Feshbach called Dr. Hare and again expounded on the corporation's relations with its shareholders and employees, which met with a rather quick and defiant answer. "Mr. Fishback, (Dr. Hare had an incredible memory but was sometimes careless with names) the way I treat my employees and future shareholders is none of your business. I won't tell Lumborg how to sell stock so don't tell me how to run my business. We'll pursue this with others." End of conversation.

Dr. Hare called a meeting in his office with Bill Rorden, Stephen Hare, Hazel Hare and me. "When we go public I think it might look strange to potential shareholders that we don't even have a salesman, let alone a sales department. We sure as hell haven't needed one with our backlog, but some day soon we might. And it'll look better when we go public."

Si Krinsky came to mind again as Dr. Hare was thinking about how to establish a sales department without going through the painful search and interviews with strangers that might take months. Si traveled all fifty states peddling products for several manufacturers, making the rounds of radio and television stations and sometimes actually making deliveries from the trunk of his car.

"From what I know about Si he is well liked and respected in the industry. If I can convince him to come in with us it's the fastest way to start a sales department."

Stephen Hare was the only one to express a negative opinion. "We haven't needed a salesmen so far and I don't think we need one now." Like his father he spoke his mind.

Krinsky wasn't easy to convince since he was not accustomed to being a part of an organization and liked his independence. But he was finally persuaded and a new subsidiary was incorporated as GRAVCO with Si as president with 20 percent of the stock.

Krinsky had a friend in New York named Murray who worked for a securities broker. Si told his friend the company was considering going public. Murray promptly got on the phone and asked to have an opportunity to handle the underwriting.

Murray was sent financial information and invited out to look at the facilities. A few days later he flew to Sacramento, rented a car and found his way to the rural area of the Grass Valley Group. Murray was short in stature and trim, no outstanding physical characteristics except when he spoke the New York accent made him seem like he was trespassing under the tall Ponderosa Pines and Live Oaks. By two o'clock he had seen all the facilities, watched the women stuffing circuit boards with components, saw metal sheared for cases, and peered over the shoulder of a technician making final tests of the equipment connected to an oscilloscope.

"I have to go back to the motel for a few minutes. I'll be back shortly," he said to me as we walked back from building No. 2 in the warm afternoon sun, partially shaded by the tall pines. Murray left and returned an hour later.

As Murray and I entered Dr. Hare's office I said, "You called your boss to tell him what you've seen?"

"Yes, I did."

"He was skeptical of the profit numbers I sent you. You were too. What did you tell him?"

"I told him I think they could be right."

A minute or so went by with no one speaking.

"We'd like to handle your issue. We can do it cheaper than any of the bigger underwriters. We'll take our fee in stock. 15 percent of the total number of shares. We can get the job done with the least expense to you."

To the surprise of Dr. Hare, I spoke quickly, "No thanks, Murray. I know all about those 'piece of the action' deals and we want no part of it. We deserve better and we'll find it."

Murray was surprised at the immediate rejection of his proposal, but offered no rebuttal.

"Keep us in mind. I have to get going to catch the red-eye back to New York," Murray said as he got up to leave.

When Murray was out the door Dr. Hare said, "You were kinda rough on him, don't you think?"

"No. I've heard about those schlock operations and I don't want us to go that route."

"With the kind of reception we've had, maybe we have to settle for the schlock type."

"I don't think so. We can do better."

Later that day Dr. Hare and I were out hitting pitch shots to one of the new greens and talking about the type of grass on the tees.

"Incidentally, you never did tell me what all this new grass cost," Dr. Hare smiled as he laid a ball down on the tee.

"I guess that's right. I didn't."

We went ahead with our little game. Dr. Hare never again asked about the cost of the turf.

After three unsatisfactory attempts to find a broker it was decided the whole story of the company was not being evaluated properly with just financial statements showing three outstanding years of growth and profits. A booklet was prepared similar to a corporate annual report describing in detail the products of the company, the market and potential markets, and the competition. It included a history of the product developments and a background of the officers and financial numbers since inception. With a two-color cover and plastic binding it was very professionally done.

At the suggestion of John Markham a copy was mailed to the New York manager of Bacon, Whipple & Company with a covering letter suggesting he might be able to recommend an underwriter. A week later I received a call from the Bacon & Whipple manager, not from New York, but from its home office in Chicago.

"On the plane to Chicago I read the report you sent me and have talked with Bill Bacon. We've made a few telephone calls inquiring about you and Dr. Hare and received accolades about you both. We would like to handle the underwriting."

"That surprises me since I had been told you didn't handle anything that small," I answered.

"Never mind about that. We're interested and Bill Bacon would like to come down some time next week to talk about it."

"Sounds good to me. Any day will be all right. Just let us know." I had a good idea who they talked to.

William T. Bacon, Jr., a partner in Bacon, Whipple & Co., arrived with a completely different attitude than the two previous brokers. He was a big man, dressed in a dark blue suit. He had an easy manner, obviously was comfortable in any environment. I came to work that day in a dark suit complete with jacket and tie. Bacon asked a lot of questions, made some suggestions and concluded, "You can do almost anything you want to, within reason. We'll split the stock and you don't have to set the price until the very last minute."

During lunch, another typically tasty spread by Hazel, Bacon emphasized the company should have a law firm well experienced in preparing the legal work for stock offerings and a nationally known accounting firm to do the auditing and prepare the financial statements. When the lunch was over and they were relaxing on the deck looking out over the terrain, Dr. Hare took me aside.

In a subdued tone he said, "Just what the hell do you think you're doing?"

"Whattaya mean?"

"The dark suit and tie."

"We haven't been doing too good and I thought maybe they're taking us for just mountain folks so I thought I'd dress like they do. I didn't like the way the others talked down to us."

"You listen to me. When we go to their place we dress the way they do. Here we do as we please. If they judge us by the way we dress I don't want to have a damn thing to do with them." He squinted one eye and made one nod of his head which meant "And I mean it." We rejoined Bacon and drove back down to the office for more talk about the details of a public stock offering.

When Bacon left it was well understood that Bacon, Whipple & Co. would be the underwriters of the initial public offering.

I had a nodding acquaintance with "Rip" Miller, a partner in Arthur Young & Company which did the annual audit of the Sangamo Electric Company for years. It was easy for me to call its Chicago office and get someone from the San Francisco office to come to Grass Valley. Luckily this was in the summer, the slackest season of the year for accounting firms, so a senior accountant arrived at Grass Valley a few days later.

A dull gray vintage Bentley, the first ever in the area, rolled up the driveway of the Grass Valley Group and out stepped a tall dignified gentleman. Perhaps because of the car, he even looked British. Turned out he was British. Douglas Page was his name. After the introductions and his almost-apology for the Bentley, as there was no intention of his being pretentious driving a ten-year-old car, we got down to the business of accounting. Since the company did not have certified audits for the past five years, they would have to audit the records for that period, which would take quite a few man hours. He estimated the cost between $25,000 and $30,000.

The audit went smoothly until they got to the inventory of the Work in Progress. Jim Ward, the lead accountant, and I had anticipated the problem as it had been valued on a formula based on percentage of completion. It was Dr. Hare's method, but it did not fit "generally accepted accounting principles." The total dollars was not in question, just the method. Ward and I were doing the re-pricing to suit the accountants when Dr. Hare found out about it.

"There's not a damn thing wrong with my method!" His voice reverberated off the walls. He picked up a pencil and on his yellow legal pad went through his formula step by step, like he was teaching math to a couple of under-graduates. He didn't take kindly to the non-committal attitude of his two listeners.

"I have to certify that inventory is its true value and I won't sign anything I don't agree with. We can chuck this whole thing before I'll do that!" He was riled.

"Look, I did some samples using a method they say is acceptable and we're going to come out with almost the same values. I'll show it to you when we're finished and you will agree it is correct. Guarantee it." I mollified the Doctor as I had more than once. The inventory valuation was never a subject of conversation again.

On the day the numbers were to be finished Bill Bacon flew in from Chicago. He really didn't disbelieve the profit we had shown him in our initial report, but it was obvious he was apprehensive some ugly snake might be kicked up in the audit. When the accountants showed their statements there was a sigh of relief and almost a celebration. Bacon went back to Chicago confident he was going to have a successful initial public offering.

During the weeks of the audit both Dr. Hare and I worked with Peter Platt, the attorney with Brombeck, Phleger & Harrison, writing drafts for the prospectus. Peter was in his thirties, a graduate of Yale with a Yale accent similar to that of Chick Lanphier. He was an immaculate dresser, always well groomed. Casual for him meant discarding the jacket. He had several large corporate clients such as a gold mining company and a producer of gypsum products. Prospectuses of companies that had recently gone public were handed around for us to use as a guide on the type of information about the company that had to be put together besides the financial statements.

With all the profit numbers now official, several decisions had to be made. How many times to split the stock and what price to put on it. Bacon was euphoric about the numbers and the prospects for future earnings.

"I'll be honest with you. With those numbers you can pick any price you want and we'll sell it. I do think it's wise to not set it too high because you may want to come back to the well again some day. If the stock performs well in the after market it will make the next time easy. Another favorable factor is that management is not selling out. You will still have over 60 percent of the company. That indicates you have confidence in the future. You don't decide the price now. Wait until the day before it comes out."

In a few weeks the registration statement was filed with the Securities and Exchange Commission. The attorneys for both the company and the broker and Dr. Hare went to Washington, D. C. The attorneys argued over changes the

SEC wanted and finally settled on a preliminary prospectus which was printed overnight. Before Dr. Hare left Washington, Bacon told him they had to have a "Due Diligence" meeting.

"What the hell is a 'Due Diligence' meeting?" asked Dr. Hare. The broker explained it was a procedure required by the Securities and Exchange Commission so that brokers or analysts could ask questions to be sure they have exercised due diligence before selling the stock to the public. Theoretically it protects the public from securities which had not been thoroughly looked into by the brokers. But it also protects the brokers from law suits brought by losing investors if the brokers can show they exercised good judgment in learning about all aspects of the company. A date was set for the meeting to be held in Chicago at the offices of Bacon, Whipple & Co. A preliminary prospectus, called a "Red Herring," was printed on October 11, 1967, and distributed to the participating underwriters. Bacon, Whipple reserved some shares for employees of the company and the word was passed around along with a list for them to sign up for the number they wanted to buy.

"Did you call Chick and ask him how many shares he wanted?" Dr. Hare asked me.

"Yes. 500."

"500? Wonder what the ...." Obviously he was disappointed, but let it pass without finishing his comment.

The day finally came for the last lawful requirement before a stock could be offered to the general public. Dr. Hare flew to Chicago for the "Due Diligence" meeting, looking to it with some apprehension since he did not know what to expect. On the plane he reviewed all of the financial data in the prospectus to make sure he would not misspeak.

La Salle Street was the financial center of Chicago, home of brokers, underwriters and bankers. 135 South had the solid and substantial look of 1920s architecture, gray stone and red brick. The address alone communicated success. Ghosts of king-makers ride the polished brass filigreed elevators along with the dark blue and gray flannel suits and the secretaries in proper Chanel jackets. The offices of Bacon, Whipple were paneled in wood, darkened with age. Tall narrow windows looked out to the street and other buildings. Chairs were brought in from several of the private offices to the conference room to accommodate the visiting underwriters. About twenty stockbrokers and analysts from firms handling the underwriting milled about, shaking hands. Most were acquainted with each other from previous such occasions. Murray was there from New York and had been busy bending Bill Bacon's ear. The taller Bacon bent his head down to hear his persistent pursuer, finally easing away and calling the meeting to order.

"Good afternoon, gentlemen. Thank you for coming." The noise level dropped, the chatter ceased. The few standing in back took their seats.

"You have had the opportunity to examine the 'Red Herring' and no one can better answer any questions you may have than Dr. Donald Hare, president and chairman of the Grass Valley Group. I do have a short comment. We have spent many hours at the company in the past few months and it certainly is a unique operation in a beautiful setting in the foothills of the Sierras. Dr. Hare."

Dr. Hare stood up looking every bit the part of a CEO, dressed in a brown Harris tweed sport coat, white shirt, natty tie and black rimmed glasses. His smile radiated confidence. He was teaching again.

"Good afternoon, gentlemen. This is my first experience at going public with information I have always considered private, except for the bank and the IRS. I understand why you are here and I think I can best serve that purpose by taking your questions." He smiled and nodded to the first to raise his hand.

"Dr. Hare, I notice that in 1966 the American Broadcasting Company was your largest customer, contributing to 37 percent of sales. Does that bother you?" asked the broker.

"Frankly, yes. It's not as bad as that old axiom that the man who has only one customer does not sleep well at night. But there is a reason for it. ABC is responsible for getting us into the television equipment business. They had an urgent need for some equipment three years ago and we delivered on time and with quality. It established a good relationship. The station engineers in Los Angeles and San Francisco are creative, eager to try new methods, new special effects. They call Bill Rorden, our chief engineer, and hatch up some new piece of equipment. Two years ago we had two models of video equipment and several of audio; we now have 70 and that relationship is responsible for many of them. Also ABC is independent from any manufacturer. RCA and NBC are related. So are Columbia and CBS. That's a hard nut to crack."

He continued. "Obviously, if ABC should take a moratorium on capital investment it could put a dent in our sales.

We are getting more market share now than we have in the past. A number of television stations are insisting on certain pieces of our equipment in their orders to the large companies. I feel ABC will always be a large customer, but percentage-wise they should be less significant. Remember, we never had a sales department until recently."

Another raised his hand, "You have had a fantastic growth in both sales and profits. Do you feel you can continue at this rate?"

"This year is going to be great. We have a backlog that will carry over into the first quarter of next year. We're working on models to be introduced next Spring at the National Association of Broadcasters which we think will be well accepted. We feel instructional television could be a substantial market in the next few years and we have added a unique line of test equipment designed especially for the television station. Barring a serious downturn in the economy I believe we can sustain close to our present rate of growth."

"Dr. Hare, I have trouble trying to decide why you are taking the company public. You don't have a lot of debt to retire. Your balance sheet is excellent. Almost all of the proceeds are not definitely earmarked for a purpose."

"I see your point. You're not the first to question this decision. We are not pressed to do this for financial reasons. By being a publicly held company we can better attract engineering talent, which we will need for sustained future growth. It improves our status as a company. For example, we can offer stock options to employees when we have a stock that can be traded. We can pursue acquisitions, we think, with better success than we have had in the past as a privately held company."

Murray finally spoke up and Dr. Hare wondered what was coming since he was upset at not being the leading underwriter. "Dr. Hare, you remember I was at your plant out there in the woods. Pretty spot, but why did you pick that area and wouldn't you be better off closer to a larger city like Sacramento or San Francisco? For a guy like me who doesn't even drive a car to work it's a hard place to get to." A few chuckles.

"I was born and raised in California," Dr. Hare said. "After completing my doctorate at Stanford I worked in Texas, New York, South Carolina and Connecticut. When I had the opportunity to locate a laboratory anyplace in the country I talked to my old acquaintance, Charlie Litton. After he sold out to Tex Thornton he bought a hospital building built during the war that was never occupied. He had more space than he needed and offered to rent me space temporarily. When Mrs. Hare and I came out we liked the surroundings and the climate. It felt good to be back in California and in the foothills."

"We ship everything airfreight. We're a little over an hour from the Sacramento airport and make a trip every day. It's not for everyone, especially if you like living in or near the city. But our employees like the natural surroundings."

Another question. "Since your competition is larger companies well established in the industry, what makes your product so special that you have been able to invade their market?"

"When we decided to give video a try we were told we were too late. That we couldn't compete with RCA, General Electric and Ball Brothers. We had some good luck and we built a quality product. Bill Rorden, my chief engineer, and I have the idea we can build anything. When we hear of a problem or a new idea from the station engineers, we sit around for a couple of hours talking about it and then get to work and design the damn thing. No committee, no drafting department, no requisitions. We just put a breadboard in the vise, pick up a soldering iron and get to work. In a couple of days we have a working model. If it is really complicated, it might take a couple of weeks. A big company like RCA takes two years to do the same thing."

"Oh yes, one more thing. We have the best guarantee in the business. Our products are guaranteed to perform to original specifications for two years or they will be repaired or replaced at no charge. If a unit fails for any reason we will have a loaner on the way, airfreight, the same day so they will have it the next day."

"What price do you expect to set on the stock?"

"We're thinking $10, but I understand we don't have to decide until the very last minute." That set some of the pencils busy and created a little chatter.

"Dr. Hare, I note you don't have any government contracts. Will you comment on that?"

"We've had some in the past. Right now we don't have time for them. We get some calls occasionally. We sell to the government anything off the shelf, same price, same terms as any other customer. But we won't build anything to government specifications." He didn't say the profit margins on government contracts were too low compared to commercial products and they did not like to do printed manuals, always part of a contract.

When the meeting was over, Bill Bacon and Dr. Hare went into Bacon's office.

"You did great. I knew you would."

"It was easier than I expected. But when Murray put up his hand I thought I might be in for something since he was disappointed he didn't get the underwriting."

"I gave him some more shares," Bacon replied.

On November 22, the day before Thanksgiving, the decision was made to put the shares on the market on the 24th at $10. Perhaps it wasn't the greatest timing since many of the Wall Street people take that Friday off. All the shares had been sold and the after market could wait until the next week. The prospectus was printed Wednesday night and in the hands of the participating underwriters Friday morning. The financial printers work twenty-four hours a day and are expert at speed-printing and fast delivery which was normal in their business.

The shares edged up in price slowly but continuously. From his house Dr. Hare brought a big brass Chinese gong that hung in a mahogany stand. It was placed in front of the blackboard in the shop and when a report of a rise in the stock price was posted, Dr. Hare would give the gong a hit with the padded mallet.

In December Peter Platt and I went to Chicago on a Friday morning to the offices of Bacon, Whipple to take delivery of the proceeds of the stock sale. Arrangements had been made in advance that the money be placed in an interest-bearing account in the Continental Bank at noon that day. Dr. Hare did not want the company to lose the interest earned over the weekend.

A stack of papers had to be signed. Bill Bacon reminded Platt and I that even though all of the stock had been sold, the company could still back out of the deal if it wished. Warren Haskins, attorney with the firm representing Bacon & Whipple, passed out the forms to be read and signed, one at a time. He made sure they were read, not just signed. He was well-built, firm chin like a good in-fighter, and moved like an athlete in his glen plaid suit. Haskins was the one who took the lead at the Securities and Exchange Commission in getting the prospectus presented the way he wanted it. This was a no-nonsense procedure which ended with Bacon giving me a check for the proceeds of the stock sale. I met for lunch with two executives of the Continental Bank and deposited the money. Platt went to Marshall Field's to shop for a couple of hours. He likes to cook and bought a huge chef's knife to take home. He carried it with him on the plane.

Dr. Hare had never been one to seek publicity about himself or his business. Company affairs were no one's business and he preferred privacy. That changed now that the company was releasing sales and profit figures publicly, and he made sure the local paper, THE UNION, printed the reports and any other news releases. There was only one reader in the county that he particularly wanted to reach, his former landlord and ex-friend, Charlie Litton.

A public corporation had some advantages. It made negotiating for acquisitions easier and stock option plans could make the company more attractive to engineering and management talent. "It's almost like we can print money," Dr. Hare said after realizing what new leverage the company now had. With it were some responsibilities for the behavior of employees that go beyond the plant doors.

Even though Si Krinsky's friend Murray was disappointed he didn't get the underwriting, he touted the stock and there were times it was suspected he might have affected the price. There were a limited number of shares on the market and no great number trading daily, so a sudden moderate demand could raise the price. He called me often for information and was turned down, but he persisted. Occasionally he said he heard the company had such and such big order and wanted to know if it was true and how that would affect sales for the quarter. I called Si and told him he had to quit talking to Murray about company business or he could get the company in trouble. Dr. Hare was so mad at Si he wouldn't take his calls. "Don't let him talk to me. If I do I'll fire him and I don't want to," he said. Si had a problem understanding why Dr. Hare was always "out on the property" when he called and had to settle for me. A member of an investment group in California came in one day and wanted to look around. Unfortunately for him, Dr. Hare found out who he was.

"I don't like you buying quantities of our stock," he told the startled visitor.

"Why? It shows we have confidence in your operation."

"There's not that many shares and if you have a large number and for some reason decide to dump them, a lot of small stockholders get hurt. I'd rather you stay out of our market."

The man was dumbfounded. He had expected royal treatment and got a lecture instead.

As predicted, 1967 had proven to be a banner year. Sales were up 47 percent and net profit up 66 percent over 1966. Sales topped the one million mark for the first time in company history with $1.365 million. In December Dr. Hare made a trip to the Palo Alto area and came home with new enthusiasm and four new employees. He walked right up to me immediately.

"There's something I have to tell you. I broke one of my own rules. You know I've always told you 'Don't hire anyone with a beard.'" He paused. "Well, I hired a guy with a beard. At least he keeps it trimmed, not shaggy. He's an industrial graphics designer and we're going to put him to work on the design of the switcher panel and artwork. I think he'll work out." As it turned out he didn't stay around very long. The engineers hired were Robert Cobler, Jerry Sakai and Bill Barnaham. They were important to the future expansion of both engineering and production.

After the public stock offering the name of the Grass Valley Group became more widely known, particularly in the Bay Area. Struggling start-up companies and idea-men sought us out looking for investment capital or hoping to sell an invention. We took them all seriously, ready to listen to anything that had merit. Completely unexpected, an entrepreneur inventor, he looked the part, neatly trimmed beard, very articulate, showed up one day with a new device that impressed Dr. Hare, Stephen Hare and me. It was built on a two-wheel cart and looked like a fast battery charger at a gas station. A video camera mounted on the top recorded the picture on a disk and played it back on a built-in monitor. It was made specifically for golf instruction and had the advantage of being able to record the golfer's swing and replay it immediately on the little monitor screen. At that time the only instructional aids were a Polaroid camera that took a short series of still shots of a golfer's swing, and a movie camera which had the disadvantage that the pictures would not be available until several days later when the film was processed.

Each of us took turns at teeing up a ball, had his swing recorded and played back. Of course caustic criticism and snide remarks followed the replays. Obviously the three golfers were biased, possibly to the point of influencing their judgment, but they were interested in making the device. Ideas popped up such as creating a separate division to finance the sales to club professionals who couldn't pay cash for the machine, and also putting them out as rentals. The fantasizing was short-lived as the inventor called up a few days later and said he preferred to keep control of the product and try to raise his own capital to manufacture it.

A big order was received from ABC for units to be used for the first color broadcast of the Olympics from Grenoble, France, and Mexico City. The GVG units were shipped to the electrical contractor, Fischbach and Moore in Dallas, Texas where the equipment was installed in large trailers like those used at golf tournaments and other on-site broadcasts.

Dr. Hare liked to smoke one or two cigars a day. He had a taste for good cigars which were hard to find since the Cuban crisis and he went to a lot of effort to find dealers who at times had the quality he liked. If he was at his table in his office when he finished one he would go into his private bathroom, wash his hands and take a swig of mouthwash. This particular day he and I had been talking.

"Come here. I want to show you something," he said and walked into the bathroom and turned on the water in the basin. Out came flakes of brown scale and water that was slightly rust-colored.

"For many years I wanted an office with my own private bathroom. I finally got it but look what comes out of the faucet. I think the president of the company deserves clean water in his john."

"I want you to find out what's causing this and get it fixed. I had a new water heater put in not long ago but that didn't correct it."

The treasurer had been given a lot of responsibilities outside the financial area, which was to be expected in a small company. But the first thing that went through my mind was that the boss was the engineer and physicist. If he hadn't solved it, this was going to be tough. I went into town to the plumbing shop and talked to the owner. As I explained the problem, the plumber grinned. "Yeah, I know. I removed a perfectly good water heater and installed a new one. I told Dr. Hare that was not the problem, but he insisted I install a new one."

"What's the problem?" I asked. "All I've seen is copper pipes."

"You've got electrolysis. Somewhere in that building are some galvanized pipes connected to the copper. You've got to find them and replace the iron with copper."

At the close of the production shift a maintenance man and I searched for water pipes. Above the acoustic tiles in the drop ceiling of the metal shop we found the culprits, several sections of galvanized pipe. Fortunately, the pipes were exposed, none inside the concrete block walls. The new maintenance man was good at most everything, including plumbing.

"I want you to measure what it will take to replace the iron pipe with copper. Make a list of every copper fitting you will need. Go get it at the hardware store and come to me when you have it. Be sure you have everything because I want you to do this on a Saturday and you may not be able to get something if you come up short."

The engineers were the only ones who worked on Saturday so they were told the water would be shut off, perhaps all day. Drinking water was not a problem since bottled water was always available. When Dr. Hare heard about it he said, "Put in a new water heater."

"But we don't need a new water heater," came my reply. The plumbing shop owner had assured me that the present water heater, being glass-lined, would not have been affected by the scaling electrolysis.

"Put in a new one anyway."

A new water heater was added to the list.

Saturday the water was shut off, the galvanized pipes disconnected and pulled out. New copper pipes were installed and tested for leaks before the end of the day.

The president's john had clean water.

Sometime over the years Dr. Hare's palate acquired a taste for fine wines. He enjoyed several kinds but preferred a fine Bordeaux. A glass was customary with his evening meal. One glass only, since he was a self-disciplinarian and seldom over-indulged in anything. His appreciation of gourmet foods never tempted him to overeat a favorite. "Just because you like the taste is no excuse to gorge yourself," was his credo. A liquor dealer in San Francisco occasionally shipped him a case of wine with an assortment of several different labels of newly arrived vintages so he could try them and order those he liked. With a childish grin of expectation he whispered to me, "I just received a new shipment. About four o'clock let's go up to the house." We went up to his house basement room which was gradually becoming a wine cellar, armed with a corkscrew, two wine glasses, a knife and a plate of cheese. We sipped and snacked on cheese between samples and tried to describe our preferences. Being close to the president had some pleasant perks. Dr. Hare gradually accumulated an extensive collection of fine wines.

The development of the new video switcher went swiftly and was ready for demonstration at the March, 1968, National Association of Broadcasters Convention. By mid-year the company had received requests for quotes on systems totaling over a million dollars and had firm orders for five systems. Growth in sales continued at a steady pace even though its large customer, ABC, was buying very little capital equipment. After tax profit margins, which Dr. Hare monitored very carefully, were still in the 22 percent to 26 percent area which was quite remarkable. These profit margins were quite important as a measure of operating success, but never once was a product modified just to increase its gross profit. The company had an excellent balance sheet, adequate cash flow and virtually no long-term debt.

Still, Dr. Hare was a product of the Depression and the bare survival of this company just five years ago left an indelible mark. He was not about to relax and ease up his daily attention to all phases of the business. He still worked in his shop bay between interruptions of the telephone or a stroll around the buildings and the grounds.

"I never want to own a business that gets so large I won't know what's going on," was his philosophy.

Dr. Hare was not great on meetings. He said that one reason big companies are so slow in getting things done is that they spend too much time in meetings. But there were times he had to get the engineers together as a group rather than just one-on-one. For days he had been stewing about what direction the company should go with new products. It was time for an engineering meeting.

"I've looked at our sales mix for the past six months and the backlog to see exactly which models make up most of the orders. Over half of our orders are for the 900 series, but I wonder how long that will continue. There are about 800 television stations, not likely to be many more, and most of them are getting up-dated on equipment. We've got to think of new additions like the switcher. I think it has a greater potential that we haven't discovered." Dr. Hare looked at Bob Cobler.

"Bob, I'd like you to take over the switcher. The whole department. Engineering, design, the whole ball of wax."

He continued, "We're taking business away from our competitors because we have new innovations along with reliability and we've got to keep it up. Bill has good contacts with the network in L. A. and San Francisco. That's all I have, fellas."

Jerry Sakai stayed after the rest left. "I want to talk about production," he said

"What's bothering you?" Dr. Hare asked.

"There are too many screwups. Mostly on the boards. Sometimes we have to wait a week for one board to complete the final assembly of a unit."

"You think you can straighten it out?"

"Yes."

"Fine. You're the production manager."

The year 1968 established new records with a steady increase in the rate of sales growth and substantial after-tax profits.

A VISITOR

The new national status of the Grass Valley Group, its expanding production facilities, its profitability in this little former gold mining town attracted other forces the company had never before experienced. For several weeks an organizer for the International Brotherhood of Electrical Workers solicited employees to become members of the union. This was a first for Dr. Hare. His companies had always been small enough that people did whatever they did best or whatever needed to be done. There were no job descriptions, no organizational charts. He decided the pay scale for certain jobs, merit raises, vacation policies, bonuses and the company-paid medical insurance. The company was very careful to operate within state and federal wage and hour laws. The possibility of dealing with an outside organization representing employees was disturbing and certainly distracting. Dr. Hare couldn't fathom operating his own company and be prohibited from asking an employee to do something that was not within that person's job description. Not being able to give employees a bonus without asking for permission from the union was distasteful. He was proud of the working conditions he provided for employees and resented any intrusion in that area. The dress code would probably be a bargaining issue. The women were required to wear dresses, no slacks or jeans. Some didn't like it. His attitutude was of the old school: if you don't like the job, go someplace else. Once a year he was reminded too vividly of union rules at the National Association of Broadcasters convention when setting up exhibits. His own engineers couldn't do certain things without calling for a union electrician, who in turn couldn't carry a ladder. That was the job of a maintenance worker. No, he felt he had been fair to his employees and was almost paranoid at the prospect of dealing with a union. To make sure he didn't err in meeting this new situation, Dr. Hare decided he should have competent advice. He consulted the law firm of Morrison, Foerster, Holloway, Clinton & Clark, of San Francisco. James C. Paras, a partner in the firm, came to Grass Valley and advised Dr. Hare what was likely to happen and how he and management people should conduct themselves to avoid any legal problems. He was told that when the union organizer had signed up a majority of the production employees, the procedure was that they would send someone to present Dr. Hare with the signed cards of its members. Just how and when they would do this was not predictable, but Paras hinted it sometimes could be rather creative. In the following few weeks the tensions built. Telephone calls were always screened, but special care was taken when the call was for Dr. Hare. Even a car moving slowly up to the parking lot like a first-time visitor attracted notice. Dr. Hare and Hazel were jumpy, their nerves on edge.

In downtown Grass Valley, a young man stopped at a Texaco station to use the pay telephone. He looked up the number in the tattered phone book and then dialed the Grass Valley Group.

"I would like to speak to Dr. Hare."

"May I tell him who's calling?"

"Donald Spaulding."

There was no intercom. Dr. Hare didn't like them. An open switch could broadcast a private conversation. The receptionist put the telephone on hold and walked the short distance to Dr. Hare's office door, which was almost always open.

"Dr. Hare, there's a Donald Spaulding who wants to talk to you." The name didn't register. Could this be the union representative?

"Hare, here."

"This is Donald Spaulding. I think you might be my father! I would like to meet you."

After a period of silence. "Where are you calling from?"

"In Grass Valley."

"I think you should come to the plant. We're out in the county on Bitney Spring Road." Dr. Hare put down the phone, visibly disturbed. He turned to Hazel. "This guy says I might be his father."

Hazel knew her husband had married when he was in college, and that they had had a baby before divorcing. The first she even knew of that marriage was when they went to get their marriage license in Connecticut and the clerk asked if he had been married before. His answer was a bit of surprise. He explained it away as a college romance that didn't work out. She had known about his second marriage, even knew his wife, but thought it was his first. This person might be an imposter. The labor union activities had them suspicious of most everything.

"I'm expecting a Donald Spaulding. Tell him to come on in when he arrives," Dr. Hare told the receptionist.

He turned to Hazel. "Norma and I split up and got divorced right after the baby was born. She got married again and her husband adopted the child. I haven't seen or heard of either one of them since."

Hazel was silent. This was no time for a family discussion. They were both too tense about the union thing and might say something both would regret.

When the 33-year-old Donald Spaulding walked into Dr. Hare's office Hazel looked at him inquisitively to see if there was a family resemblance. He wasn't as tall as Donald, his dark hair was more curly and he had a stockier build. If he is Donald's son he must take after his mother, she concluded.

When at Stanford Donald Hare used another of his many talents, music, to earn a few dollars on weekends. He played with a band made up of several of his fraternity brothers. One was Neil Spaulding, a pianist. Neil was dating an attractive nursing school student, Norma, who regularly met him after some of their band engagements. Donald became attracted to her and wooed her away from Neil. Norma became pregnant. She and Donald were married and on July 4, 1935, Donald George Corkhill Hare Jr. was born. That summer the couple moved in with her parents. Shortly thereafter they had a very loud and stormy argument. Donald walked out and they were soon divorced. Several years later Neil appeared back on the scene, married Norma, adopted Donald Jr. and changed his name to Donald Knight Spaulding. Neil was an accomplished piano player and worked with big name bands, including those of Jimmy Dorsey and Phil Harris.

Donald Spaulding smiled as he held out his hand. He carried no briefcase, no papers.

Dr. Hare under the best of situations was not a "gladhander." His handshakes were something just barely polite under normal conditions. He stared at the young man, at first unaware of the outstretched hand, which he finally took. It was awkward. Dr. Hare looked at the son he hadn't seen since he was a baby, not since that day he and Norma had their tempestuous confrontation. And all father and son did was to shake hands. Slowly Dr. Hare recovered some from the expectation this was going to be the union representative.

"This is my wife, Hazel."

Hazel offered her hand.

"Please have a seat," she said to Donald Spaulding, pointing to the sofa.

"How did you find me?" Dr. Hare asked.

"My Grandmother has kept track of you over the years and she told me where you were, so I decided to look you up."

"What have you been doing?"

"I taught design at the University of New Mexico in Albuquerque. Right now I'm an associate teacher at the University of Nevada in Reno. I didn't have any classes today so I thought this would be a good time to find you."

The awkward situation didn't get much better as Dr. Hare was not the type to throw his arms around any relative, let alone a grown man he had not known, even if it was his son. Spaulding didn't know what to expect, but he thought the reception could have been much warmer. And, of course, he had no knowledge of the stressful situation he so untimely walked into. Another time it might have been different. The conversation dragged and became difficult after only a few minutes so Spaulding decided it was time to leave. He was disappointed.

Dr. Hare walked his son out to the car and became slightly more fatherly. "If someday I can help you in any way don't hesitate to call me," was his parting message. Donald Spaulding never saw his biological father again.

Stephen Hare was working in the shop. It never occurred to Dr. Hare to introduce the brothers. Had he thought of it he would not have been able to handle the emotional crisis of the moment. The relations were already tense between Dr. Hare and Stephen. Dr. Hare expected much of his son, perhaps too much, which met with resistance from Stephen in certain areas of their relationship. To suddenly introduce a previously unknown close family member would have only exacerbated the strained father-son relationship. Not until years later did Stephen Hare learn he had a half-brother.

MORE EXPANSION

Growth at a healthy pace continued into 1969. Three more buildings were added as orders came in faster in the first quarter than ever before, almost double those of 1968. The 120 acres with its buildings carefully spaced on the wooded hillside had taken on the look of a college campus rather than an industrial park. A new state-of-the-art plating and etching facility for metal finishing and processing printed circuit boards was put into operation. Over half of the sales were for the new video switching systems. New special effects were added to the switchers with manufacturing rights from the "Borderline" unit of Anderson Laboratories, Inc.

The following letter was received from the National Aeronautics and Space Administration:

NATIONAL AERONAUTICS AND SPACE ADMINISTRATION
MANNED SPACECRAFT CENTER
HOUSTON, TEXAS 77058

IN REPLY REFER TO: FS

Dr. Donald Hare
Bitney Springs Rd.
P. O. Box 1114
Grass Valley, California

Dear Dr. Hare:

As you are aware, the TV coverage provided during the Apollo 10 flight was unprecedented both in quantity and quality. Of particular significance was the first live color television received from a spacecraft. This achievement was realized in part through the color synchronization and processing equipment provided by your company.

The appreciation of the Manned Spacecraft Center and the viewing public is extended to you, the Grass Valley Group, Incorporated, and to Mr. Buford, who assisted in the equipment installation and training of our personnel. Your organization can take great pride in this achievement and its contribution to this nation's Manned Spaceflight Program.

Sincerely,

Brian M. Duff
Public Affairs Officer

At almost the same time a letter arrived from another governmental agency stating it was removing the Grass Valley Group from its bid offer list because GVG did not have an "approved quality control department." Dr. Hare posted both letters side by side on the bulletin boards. His conception of quality control was that everyone knew his job and took pride in his work. To him taking statistical samples in a small manufacturing company was nothing but a ruse that added to the overhead.

Instructional Television continued to be a disappointment. It appeared the educators were undecided as to how to use the medium, both hardware and software, and were also waiting for federal funding which was not forthcoming.

Improvements were made in the 900 series, GVG's bread and butter product line for two years. A new integrated circuit used in the mixing amplifier eliminated the need for studio technicians to make tedious adjustments.

PRODUCTION EMPLOYEES UNIONIZED

The International Brotherhood of Electrical Workers was successful in organizing a majority of the production and maintenance workers. They held meetings for several weeks and started negotiations with the company in June, 1969. On an average of once a week, company and union representatives met for the next three months. Not able to reach a wage agreement, an election was held by union employees to authorize a work stoppage. Dr. Hare was positive the employees would vote against a strike. Fifteen of the executives, engineers and technicians organized a pool in which each bet $5 on the vote count, the closest to take the pot. Bob Johnson knew the production employees best and hit the numbers on the nose. Dr. Hare was upset that they voted to walk, upset that he had misjudged the attitude of his employees. He was so upset that Johnson never asked for the winnings now in the safe. On August 19 the workers went on strike and assigned pickets. Dr. Hare was determined the company would operate in spite of the strike. Replacement workers were hired and production continued without interruption. The company used its electronic expertise to monitor what was going on at the picket line. Union representatives reported that no shipments were going out when actually they continued on schedule. A company officer met regularly with the union negotiator and responded to every demand, but no consensus was reached. After months of no agreement, the union filed a claim that the company did not negotiate in good faith. The NLRB ruled against the union and it eventually abandoned its effort to obtain a collective bargaining agreement with the company.

Near the end of another record year Bill Rorden had numerous telephone conversations with Jules Barnathan, vice president of engineering of ABC, on the design of a sophisticated routing switcher. Barnathan made a trip out to Grass Valley to meet with Rorden and to discuss the project with Dr. Hare. After they outlined what was involved Dr. Hare asked Bill, "How many racks will this take?"

"Eight," Bill replied.

Dr. Hare thought a minute, and turned to Barnathan. "How about $525,000?"

"Sounds all right to me," was Barnathan's reply. They shook hands. No purchase order in writing, no specs except what Rorden and Barnathan talked about.

Rorden went to New York, looked over the area and again discussed with Barnathan what they intended to do, making some notes on the back of an envelope. Later the ABC engineering department requested a Xerox copy of Bill's envelope for its records. This was the largest video and audio switching system ever fabricated by the company, or any company. It had 6,000 switches for video and 6,000 switches for audio to permit as many as sixty output destinations to select any one of a hundred sources of video and its corresponding audio. After the system was installed and operating it was later expanded to 24 racks of equipment to permit many more outputs and sources of video and audio signals.

A less sophisticated switching system was designed which allowed broadcast studios in smaller stations and institutions to select inputs from various sources such as cameras, video tape recorders and film projectors, and combine them in the production of a program.

ANOTHER MILESTONE

January 19, 1970, the company's stock was listed on the American Stock Exchange with the symbol GVG. Dr. and Mrs. Hare flew to New York to view the ticker tape as the first trade occurred. 1,300 shares were traded at 18 1/2. Another mark was achieved by Dr. Hare.

Merrill Lynch, Pierce, Fenner and Smith Inc distributed the following to its many offices:

GRASS VALLEY GROUP /GVG /

LISTED ON AMEX

```
RECENT PRICE = 18⅞
1969 PRICE RANGE = 20½ = 10¼
CURR INDIC ANN DIV RATE = NONE
P /E MULT ON 1968 EARNS OF $0.33 = 57.2
P /E MULT ON EST 1969 EARNS OF $0.50 = 37.8
GRQ INVEST DECISION = FOR APPREC , INTERMED TRM 3, LONG TRM 3
```

1. GRASS VALLEY GROUP WAS ADMITTED FOR LISTING TUESDAY ON THE AMERICAN STOCK EXCHANGE . LOCATED IN GRASS VALLEY , CALIFORNIA , APPROXIMATELY 150 MILES NORTHEAST OF SAN FRANCISCO , THIS SMALL COMPANY ENTERED THE BROADCAST EQUIPMENT FIELD IN 1963. SINCE THAT TIME ITS GROWTH FROM A SMALL BASE HAD BEEN RAPID . GVG FIRST WENT PUBLIC IN 1967.

2. BROADLY DEFINED , GVG PRODUCES LINE AND TERMINAL EQUIPMENT THAT IS USED BETWEEN THE CAMERA AND TRANSMITTER IN TELEVISION BROADCAST STATIONS , CLOSED CIRCUIT TELEVISION SYSTEMS AND , TO A LESSER EXTENT , RADIO STATIONS . THE COMPANY -S PRODUCT LINE WAS BROADENED TO INCLUDE MEASURING AND SCANNING EQUIPMENT THROUGH THE 1968 ACQUISITION OF MICRO METRIC . THE COMPANY -S PRODUCTS ARE MARKETED THROUGH ITS 80 PC OWNED SUBSIDIARY , GAVCO SALES , INCORPORATED .

3. THE OVER $400 MILLION MARKET FOR BROADCAST EQUIPMENT IS SERVICED BY AT LEAST 8 MAJOR EQUIPMENT MANUFACTURERS , THE LARGEST BEING RCA . THE FUTURE SUCCESS OF GRASS VALLEY GROUP WILL DEPEND IN LARGE MEASURE ON ITS ABILITY TO INCREASE ITS MARKET SHARE BY INTRODUCING NEW AND BETTER PRODUCTS . THE COMPANY -S DEVELOPMENT PROGRAM IS CURRENTLY EMPHASIZING THE FOLLOWING PRODUCT LINES - /1/ INSTRUCTIONAL TELEVISION /ITV / AND CLOSED CIRCUIT TELEVISION /CCTV / TEST EQUIPMENT , /2/ DISTRIBUTION AMPLIFIERS FOR ITV AND CCTV , /3/ DISTRIBUTION SWITCHING EQUIPMENT , AND /4/ COMPLETE ITV SYSTEMS .

4. MANAGEMENT RECENTLY INDICATED THE 1969 EARNINGS WOULD APPROXIMATE 50 CENTS A SHARE VS 33 CENTS AND THAT SALES WOULD BE $3.6-3.7 MILLION VS $2.2 MILLION . NINE MONTHS RESULTS WERE 39 CENTS VS 25 CENTS . THE YEAR END BACKLOG WAS ABOUT $1 MILLION , UP SHARPLY FROM THE $300,000-400,000 OF 1968 YEAR END , BUT DOWN FROM THE JUNE 1969 FIGURE OF $1.5 MILLION .

5. OF THE 1,480,073 SHARES OUTSTANDING , ABOUT 53.8 PC ARE CONTROLLED BY MANAGEMENT .

COMMENT -- WHILE WE DO NOT EXPECT THE VERY HIGH GROWTH RATES OF THE PAST TO BE MAINTAINED , WE DO FEEL THAT WITH INCREASED MARKET SHARE , PENETRATION OF NEW DEVELOPING MARKETS SUCH AS ITV , AND NEW PRODUCT INTRODUCTION , GVG CAN SHOW GOOD GROWTH IN THE YEARS AHEAD . OUR ESTIMATED EARNINGS THIS YEAR IS 60 TO 75 CENTS A SHARE VS 50 CENTS . SO LARGE A RANGE IS NECESSITATED BY THE HIGH DEGREE OF UNCERTAINTY IN THE ECONOMIC OUTLOOK FOR 1970. SALES COULD TOP THE $5 MILLION LEVEL . THE SHARES OF THIS SMALL COMPANY SELL AT A HIGH MULTIPLE AND MUST BE REGARDED AS VERY SPECULATIVE . FOR THIS REASON WE WOULD ONLY SUGGEST PURCHASE ON A LONG TERM BASIS /IN HIGH RISK ACCOUNTS / AS PART OF A PACKAGE APPROACH TO EMERGING HIGH TECHNOLOGY COMPANIES .

SEC RCH ~TO 441P

The increased exposure to national markets created an interest in the company as well as its products and superb balance sheet. An acquisition representative from ITT showed up one day and expressed an interest in the company. Dr. Hare responded dispassionately to his questions until the man asked, "Just what are your goals for the next five years?"

"Hell, I'm not sure what they are for next week, let alone five years. We don't waste our time making five-year plans," was the reply. That brought the visit to an early conclusion.

The increased size of the complex, now over 300 acres and five buildings, caused concern for more security from forest fires. New ponds were dug and connected with water pipes, and gasoline powered pumps with fire hoses were stationed at each one. The fire lanes were widened, especially in the areas thick with Manzanita bushes.

For the first time in four years, 1970 was a year of reversals, but none serious. It started off with the continued fast growth rate of previous years which lasted through the first nine months. But much of it was making shipments out of a backlog not being replenished with new orders. The television networks and stations were in good financial condition, but in a frugal mood because of the approaching ban on cigarette advertising. The industry was afraid its advertising revenue would be seriously diminished. The general economy of the country was down and several GVG competitors had year-end losses. One went into Chapter XI. The profit for the year was not another record high, but it was respectable.

The lull in new orders offered the engineers an opportunity and incentive to develop fully automated systems that could be programmed in advance to eliminate human errors at "panic" periods in the stations' control rooms, such as during station breaks. The memory bank was enlarged to take up to a full year of programming that could be modified at any time. It also could be interfaced so the stations' business computers could be programmed to automatically bill customers for programs and commercials as soon as they were broadcast.

For the first time GVG started looking seriously overseas to market its products. In May it made a presentation of the automated switching equipment at the International Television Symposium at Montreux, Switzerland. It is the equivalent of the U. S. annual NAB convention. That contact culminated in a sales distribution agreement with Intertec S. A. It was followed with visits to Japan and Australia and a distribution agreement with Applied Electronics, Ltd., in Canada.

Shipments for 1971 continued to slide the first nine months as a result of the reduced orders in 1970. Sales offices were opened in six major cities. In the fourth quarter orders rebounded dramatically, not soon enough to overcome the slow first three quarters, but the year was still profitable. An avalanche of new orders heralded that 1972 would be a banner year.

And it was. In the first nine months sales of $3.2 million exceeded the sales for the entire year of 1971. Orders were coming in at the rate of $500,000 a month. Large systems were delivered to WWL-TV, New Orleans, and NBC in New York. The smaller switchers contributed to the volume in sales to non-broadcast customers for use in educational institutions, industrial training facilities, churches and cable television. The company's products were now widely accepted by the industry with no one customer accounting for more than 5 percent of the sales. At yearend sales rose to $4,658,000 and profits almost doubled 1971 to 72 cents a share. The company paid its first-ever dividend to shareholders.

AN OLD ITCH, A NEW CHALLENGE

For several years when Dr. Hare mentioned the subject of flying his own airplane, Hazel managed enough opposition to discourage any efforts in that direction. During the lean days it was easy; he couldn't afford it. But it never completely went away. Perhaps it was the new-found prosperity and the association with Bill Rorden making weekend trips in his own plane. More probably it was the challenge he had not finished since World War II: that of getting a pilot's license. He assuaged Hazel's trepidations by suggesting that she take flying lessons along with him. The tactic was obvious. It removed the argument that he might go off flying by himself, have an accident and leave her alone. With her as a trained co-pilot they would have more security.

Just taking flying lessons and getting a license was not enough. In his own mind that cleared the way for something bigger. Dr. Hare and Rorden organized a new corporation, Golden Empire Aviation. It was to be a fixed- base operation at the Nevada County Airpark to service all the needs of the private flying public. They hired an experienced pilot and mechanics and purchased a twin-engine Cessna 401-A. The most convenient way to travel to and from the Grass Valley and Nevada City area was undeniably by air as some 300 aircraft flew in and out weekly. The new company offered many services such as lessons, scenic flights, air ambulance and charter. The firm flew then-Gov. Ronald Reagan to several California cities. But Dr. Hare and Rorden grossly over-estimated the projected business and underestimated how difficult it was to make a profit in the aviation servicing business. Dr. Hare should have taken a page from Chick Lanphier's book. His company bought a similar but larger operation and lost a million dollars a year for ten years.

Not satisfied with just learning to fly the twin-engine Cessna, Dr. Hare and Hazel made trips to Phoenix, Arizona, where he and Hazel enrolled in the Sawyer Aviation School. At age 65, Dr. Hare was the oldest to complete its course and receive an instrument rating. Later, Hazel also received her multi-engine and instrument flying ratings.

NEW GOALS ATTAINED

The product development in 1972 produced a new model video switcher introduced at the March, 1973 convention of the National Association of Broadcasters. The model provided for mixing new state-of-the-art special effects with a smoother transition and softer dissolves producing "electronic vignettes." In previous years new model demonstrations created interest resulting in future orders. This new model was so well received that orders for more than $400,000 of the equipment were taken right at the show. By June 30 the company's sales backlog rose to over $2,000,000, and in spite of efforts to increase production, by fall it rose another half-million. The company was now global, with sales representation in 25 countries, including several in South America and Australia.

In the Spring Dr. Hare received a call from Earl Wantland of Tektronix in Beaverton, Oregon, indicating a desire to talk about a merger. Dr. Hare knew the company well, especially Paul Vollum, who started the company. During the past few years several other companies had made overtures to which Dr. Hare expressed little or no interest. This was different for several reasons.

Dr. Hare had great respect for Vollum, who started Tektronix with very little capital and an idea that he could build an oscilloscope that filled a need in the developing electrical and electronic industry. His success was based on good engineering and making quality products. This they had in common.

"I bought one of his early scopes. Serial No. 4, as I recall," Dr. Hare said.

The fast and continuous growth of the Grass Valley Group was a source of pride. He particularly enjoyed writing quarterly and annual reports when he could point to new technical advances and exceptional profits on increased sales. It wasn't the money; the numbers were a measure of success. But something was missing.

Administrative decisions consumed more of Dr. Hare's time. Expansion called for more space, more production employees, more engineers to be hired and the growth had to be continued to be fair to the young talent. He spent fewer hours in his research bay doing what he liked best. Some days his hot soldering iron stood undisturbed in its stand. A partially completed breadboard remained locked in the vise, untouched, for so long Dr. Hare had to mentally review the logic of the circuit he was trying to construct. He understood why Bill Rorden left Varian.

Dr. Hare could delegate more of his administrative duties; he had already relinquished some of them. But he had said many times he never wanted his company to get so big he didn't know what was going on. It was headed in that direction.

Hazel Hare noticed her husband was visibly more tired in recent months. Perhaps it was a symptom of a circulatory problem that was discovered later that required surgery. Or it could be he was no longer mentally stimulated by the daily routines that replaced the challenges for survival he had become accustomed to over the years. She would have no objection to a merger with a company like Tektronix.

A group of engineers from the Oregon electronic products manufacturer spent several days observing the operation of all the departments of the Grass Valley Group. They listened to Dr. Hare and Bill Rorden and asked questions of other engineers, becoming familiar with the products in process.

Many telephone calls later, Dr. Hare, Hazel Hare and Rorden flew up to Beaverton to have some serious talks about a merger. Dr. Hare took with him the latest financial numbers. For the first time in his life he was bargaining from a true position of strength. The Grass Valley Group had a reputation for innovative products, spectacular growth and fantastic profits. The company had a balance sheet that would make a corporate raider drool. There was no compelling reason, and hence no pressure, for a merger other than what was good for the shareholders.

The first round of talks established a mutual interest in a merger and a general plan of how the two organizations would mesh. Nothing definitive about financial considerations was discussed other than there would be no cash buyout, strictly a stock swap that would meet the requirements for a non-taxable exchange.

Since the officers of the Grass Valley Group held 52 percent of the company's stock it was obvious that if and when a satisfactory agreement was agreed to, it would be easy to get the additional votes for the necessary two-thirds approval of the shareholders.

On August 6, 1973, the officers of the Grass Valley Group flew to Beaverton again for the purpose of signing a Memorandum of Agreement for the merger of the two companies. Dr. Hare was not satisfied with the exchange ratio of Grass Valley Group stock for Tektronix shares offered in the negotiations with Earl Wantland. Dr. Hare and Vollum held a private discussion for about an hour and they came to an understanding. A Memorandum of Agreement was signed which set in motion the preparation of the final agreement subject to approval of the Boards of Directors of both companies and the shareholders of the Grass Valley Group. Under the proposed merger, Grass Valley Group shareholders would exchange 3.20717 shares of Grass Valley Group stock for each share of Tektronix stock. On August 10, 1973, the closing price of Tektronix on the New York Stock Exchange was $40.375 and the closing price of Grass Valley Group stock on the American Stock Exchange was $10.50

When word of the agreement was announced not everyone was happy. A number of engineers with the American Broadcasting Company were shareholders of the Grass Valley Group. As shareholders they had no objection to the merger. But as engineers who had dealt with GVG for years, they had their reservations. Immediately they had an engineering meeting.

Too many times they had seen a smaller company merged into a large corporate entity only to become a division with new management, new philosophy and no longer responsive to customer needs. Large companies invariably set up management barriers that resist innovations or delay them with endless committee meetings. They recalled their experience with RCA when they asked for some minor changes in its video cameras, only to be ignored. When the Grass Valley Group entered the video terminal equipment business RCA was a formidable competitor. In a few years the ability and expertise of Bill Rorden and Dr. Hare in responding to new ideas, RCA went out of the business and became a customer of the Grass Valley Group.

La Verne Pointer, chief engineer of ABC, said, "When we had an idea we'd call up or go out and see Bill Rorden. Bill would take out an envelope, ask some questions and make some notes. And we'd hear from him right away. Not weeks and months later. We didn't want to lose that."

After the meeting Tektronix got a call from Jules Barnathan, vice president, engineering, of the American Broadcasting Company. ABC's fears were expressed and advice was given to operate the Grass Valley Group as it had always been. The management of Tektronix knew ABC was a valuable customer and a valuable contributor to new ideas in the industry which had resulted in the group becoming the leader. Rorden, Bob Cobler and Jerry Sakai were to be vice presidents of the surviving subsidiary, which was of some solace to the engineers at ABC.

Aside from the written merger agreement Dr. Hare was asked to stay on for two years as a manager while the new management sent down from the parent observed and gradually assumed control. Theoretically this would assure a continuance of the operating philosophy of the original company.

Predictably, it did not work out. Dr. Hare was given one description of his role in management and the parent company's choice of manager was given a conflicting view of his responsibilities. It didn't take Dr. Hare long to discover the ambiguity. He didn't like it, called for a showdown and packed his belongings.

Although he was no longer physically present in the plant, Dr. Hare's resolution for quality work and customer satisfaction remained ingrained with those who worked for him.

On the 25th anniversary of the inception of the Grass Valley Group, Tektronix put on a media bash at the National Association of Broadcasters Convention. Visitors to Las Vegas arriving by air passed by a GVG booth handing out brochures; on their taxi ride into town they passed a large billboard touting the anniversary party; two large semi-trailers with the GVG logo were parked in strategic locations near the headquarters of the convention. Even the TV's in the hotel rooms had a startup video of the company's special graphics. The two-story high exhibit in the convention hall was by far the most expensive and elaborate display of the newest state of the art for television. Tektronix sent a camera crew and interviewer to Paradise Valley and made a documentary video with Dr. Hare and Bill Rorden relating early experiences in the company. Dr. Hare, Mrs. Hare and Bill Rorden were invited special guests to the celebration in La Vegas.

Bill Rorden   Jerry Sakai   Hazel Hare   Dr. Hare
At NAB convention, 25th anniversary of Grass Valley Group

PARADISE VALLEY, ARIZONA

During their flying lesson days at Sawyer Aviation the Hares became familiar with the Phoenix area. Now that they were leaving Grass Valley, the desert city was high on their list of places to re-locate. A residence to suit them had to have three essentials: a safe place for the puppies to play, a large area for a workshop and laboratory, and a room that could be converted to a climate-controlled wine cellar for Dr. Hare's collection of fine wines.

They found a suitable newly constructed house, high on the side of Mummy Mountain in Paradise Valley. A small amount of remodeling had to be done such as building a carport, because the large garage was going to be the shop and laboratory. Dr. Hare made a deal with Tektronix and bought his entire research bay, including the instruments, which was moved to Arizona along with their furniture and the wine collection.

There were no days of retirement inactivity for the Hares. They took computer programming lessons at the college, Spanish lessons from a renowned teacher, and traveled in their twin-engine Cessna. They squeezed in a twenty-day boat trip down the Colorado River through the Grand Canyon. One willing, but reluctant, participant was Dr. Hare. When he learned they were limited to a certain amount of luggage he carefully measured out twenty days of his daily ration of J & B scotch.

Hazel and Donald on the Colorado

Some of the Hares' activities were slowed temporarily by surgery to replace a section of Dr. Hare's aorta, which had developed aneurysms. After he recovered they flew to Europe on the Concorde and spent some time in Spain trying out their new proficiency in Castilian Spanish. Dr. Hare felt there was a total lack of a good textbook on grammar in the Spanish language so he set about to write one.

Back in the United States Dr. Hare and Hazel were invited to a meeting of concerned citizens to listen to Dr. George Roche, president of Hillsdale College, Hillsdale, Michigan. The college in its 150 years never discriminated against any student because of sex or race, and never took one penny of federal aid. It refused to report to the government the makeup of its student body by sex and race so some bureaucrat could set quotas. The government agency couldn't stand for an upstart like Hillsdale to get away with educating students without some government control, so it took the college to court. In one of the most outlandish decisions reflecting the broad powers of the government, the court ruled against the college. Although Hillsdale did not directly receive any government funds, the court ruled that since some of its students had government loans, which some of the money could be used to pay tuition, it was therefore a "recipient institution."

This rallied a group of freedom-loving Americans who already had misgivings about the direction education was heading under federal government control. The Hares flew to Hillsdale to learn more about the college. They came away impressed. The college raised its own funds for student loans and notified prospective students of its own financial aid program. From then on no admission was granted to anyone who had a government loan.

Dr. Hare made the college the beneficiary of a substantial irrevocable trust with the proviso the college was still refusing to take federal funds. He and Hazel were doing a lot of flying around the country and he was one never to leave anything to chance, no matter what the odds. Just in case some untimely accident occurred to both of them, he wanted to be sure the provisions of the trust were carried out.

The Hares visited me in Tucson and explained how and why they were interested in Hillsdale College.

"I want to be sure my wishes are carried out. You know how I feel about these things. I know you think the same way. Would you accept being one of the trustees of my estate just to be sure?" Dr. Hare asked of me. The obvious answer was "yes."

The college offered Dr. Hare an honorary degree. He declined. "I got mine the hard way," was his reply.

Later, Hazel Hare was elected to the board of trustees of Hillsdale College. She is very active in the affairs of the institution.

Dr. Hare continued with his experimentation in his shop and laboratory. Confronted with a hearing loss, he experimented with active filters to correct the problem by changing the frequencies of selected sounds to make them more understandable rather than just amplifying all sounds. He was critical of the hearing-aid manufacturers for failure to adapt new technology to their product.

Dr. Hare still missed the action of a going company with its challenges. For a few years he ran a small operation importing fine wines.

Johnnie Bulla, former airline pilot, professional golfer who could break par playing either right or left handed, and golf course designer, had an original idea how golf clubs should be constructed. A mutual acquaintance introduced Johnnie to Dr. Hare. They tried to form a company, and spent several hours hitting golf balls with clubs modified in Hare's shop. They couldn't agree on control of the company so Johnnie sold his idea to a going golf club manufacturer. I heard the story from each of them.

Dr. Hare called and asked me to search for a small company that needed financial assistance and that had interesting possibilities. Several months of looking into leads from a bank turned up only unexciting businesses with little or no future. I enrolled in a community college electronics course taught at a local manufacturer's plant hoping to learn of an engineer who might like to start his own company. That effort produced nothing, but I heard of three Ph.D. graduates of the University of Arizona, all employed by different companies who wanted to start their own company. One had his own consulting service in Tucson; one worked locally for a California company; the third worked in California. Their degrees were in optical science. All three had worked on the construction of the Multi-Mirror Telescope on Mt. Hopkins. They were confident there was a market for highly technical precision glass products. Over a period of several weeks an operating plan was put together with Dr. Hare putting up all of the financing. After one Sunday meeting at his house he said, "This is what I tried to do when I started the Grass Valley Group. I wanted to work with several scientists who were interested in developing new products. Maybe I'm going to get my wish."

He was much impressed with these young men and was more generous in the plan to finance it than one would have thought. But a dispute over who would have future control of the corporation resulted in terminating the effort.

Dr. Hare continued experimenting with a device that changed certain frequencies of sound to make voice communications more understandable to those with a common hearing deficiency. He invited me to work with him. For five days my wife and I stayed at the Hares' while I worked with him in his laboratory. I drilled holes in circuit boards, soldered components, things I had never done before with him.

He was never an early riser and normally liked to start work about 9:00 in the morning. Generally, I get up early so I went out to the shop about 6:30 or 7:00. After two days he showed up early, a little grumpy, but he wouldn't let me get ahead of him.

It was a very special week of my life.

On Christmas Day, 1984, Dr. Hare died while sitting at his computer. He was 77.

The next day a Christmas greeting card arrived in the mail. Below the printed message was the following:

"Sometime let's get together for a drink."

Signed... Corky

BIBLIOGRAPHY

Columbia University, Division of War Research, Airborne Instruments Laboratory, *Completion Report, Contract No.OEMsr-20,* Mineola, New York.

Encyclopedia of Religion, Page 180, Volume 13, 1987 Macmillan Publishing Company, New York.

Hare, John Daniel II and Norma Quarles Hare, unpublished document,*The Ancestors and the Descendents of Jacob and Mary Ann Corkhill.*

Isberg, R.A., associate of Dr. Hare at Airborne Instrument Laboratory, documents and publications.

Jacobs, Harry N., long time associate of Donald Hare at Airborne Instrument Laboratory and American Broadcasting Company.

Jensen, Homer, *The Airborne Magnetometer, Scientific American,* June, 1961.

Moore, Ronald M., unpublished document, *Early Phycisians in Fresno-Madera County Medical Society.*

The National Cyclopedia of American Biography Vol. M pp. 505, James T. White & Company, Clifton, N J.

The National Cyclopedia of American Biography Vol. 58 pp.112, James T. White & Company, Clifton, N. J.

The Texaco Star, The Power of Their Vision. The Texas Company.